40p

WATERWAY
CONSERVATION

The restored Flatford Dock on the River Stour.

WATERWAY
CONSERVATION

PETER H. CHAPLIN

with a Foreword by
JOHN HUMPHRIES
Vice Chairman of the Environment Council

Whittet Books

First published 1989

© 1989 by Peter H. Chaplin

Whittet Books Ltd, 18 Anley Road, London W14 0BY

Design by Richard Kelly

The line illustrations on pp.27, 30, 33, 37, 38, 47, 58-9, 60, 61, 65, 75
and 77 are by John Cox.

The line illustrations on pp 31, 34, 40, 41, 42, 45, 82 and 83 are by
Derek Cox.

The author and publisher are grateful to the following for kind
permission to reproduce photographs on the pages indicated:
John Marriage of River Stour Trust, p. 2; Hugh McKnight, p. 46, p. 47,
p. 54 (2); Senior Fisheries Officer, Thames Water Authority, p. 64.
All other photographs are from the author's collection.

British Library Cataloguing in Publication Data
Chaplin, Peter H. (Peter Harrison), *1922-*
Waterway conservation.
1. Great Britain. Inland waterways.
Conservation
I. Title
386'.0941

ISBN 0–905483–72–3

Contents

To my sons Paul and Thomas;
also *Grebe*,
who has taken us
far and wide
on our inland waterways.

Foreword

When Peter Chaplin asked me to do a brief foreword to his splendid new book I was delighted and deeply flattered. As a life long boatman myself *and* a keen environmentalist I have always been an advocate of the need for careful use of our precious waterway heritage, but Peter himself has been pre-eminent in this field far longer than me. He is well known with his family for their lengthy voyages by boat all over our complex waterway system. As a provider of a 'riparian owner's service' he has made his living quite literally working by the water's edge. In his determination that this work should always be conservation based he has sometimes got at cross purposes with water authorities, but he has never relaxed his determination that what is done must be environmentally sensitive.

I can think of nobody better qualified than Peter to write authoritatively on this subject and to carry forward the principles which we, at the Water Space Amenity Commission, first launched fifteen years ago. Water fauna and flora are indeed safe in Peter's hands and will be in those who read this book carefully and put into practice the wise counsels that it contains.

John Humphries
Vice Chairman
The Environment Council

Introduction

As we near the end of the twentieth century it is apparent that not only has leisure afloat become part of everyday life, but there are indications that the owning of boats will become even more commonplace with increasing leisure time and more affluent living: there will be many people, and of course boats, using the rivers and canals of this country.

Navigable waterways are here for all of us to enjoy: however it behoves us to ensure that the great heritage of our waterways is well maintained, which will mean exercising discipline – and self-discipline – in certain directions.

More powered craft on our waters means more wash, more wash leads to more erosion of the banks, more erosion of the banks means loss of waterside flora, loss of waterside flora reduces feeding, living and nesting sites for wildlife.

If that is not enough, remember that badly eroded banks have to be made good and if this is done the easy way it will probably mean the driving of interlocking steel sheets which inhibit both flora and fauna.

Constructional and maintenance work on our rivers and canals is normally carried out to sound engineering standards, but in many cases it lacks the foresight, skills and knowledge of the landscape architect, conservation officer or fishery consultant. I sincerely hope, therefore, that the following chapters will elucidate these remarks by giving straightforward information based on practical experience.

Peter H. Chaplin
Sunbury-on-Thames,
November 1988

1

History of Waterways

In Britain we have over 200 river systems, which since time immemorial have been used by man, not only for fishing and providing water for his domestic needs, but as a means of communication. Before early man commenced the art of animal husbandry to provide meat, milk and eggs, he had already mastered the skill of making rafts and crude craft so that he could travel on, and cross, water. This early navigation was often of prime importance, in fact essential, in order to sustain life in primitive communities who were dependent on their hunting and fishing abilities. The earliest evidence of inland waters of Britain being used for the planned transport of goods goes back to the Bronze Age, with the building of Stonehenge. Latest research indicates that the Preseli stone for these ancient works was brought down from the hills on the river Daugleddau. Recent discoveries during the building of the M25 bridge over the Thames near Runnymede revealed old timber piles which indicated that there may have been some sort of wharf at this point in the neolithic age.

Craft of this period would have been rafts of logs lashed together with thongs made from the stems of climbing plants, or animal hides; the coracle was the utility one-man craft of the day, being built with a framework of withies or slithers of ash and covered with hide which was laced into place with thongs made from the same material. Modern coracles are much the same in design and construction, the exception being that the covering is now of tarred canvas. They are difficult to propel against a strong current but can be lifted out of the water and carried across a broad pair of shoulders with the greatest of ease, which would obviate the problem of negotiating obstacles.

From the coracle was developed the skin covered boat with a frame and keel to facilitate progress against the current. Propulsion would have been with oars, or sometimes a sail like the ancient curraghs of Ireland; steering would in all probability been with a sweep or oar. These longer craft were more demanding and required navigational facilities. Their crews, although in no way engineers, understood the art of making weirs by driving willow stakes into the bed, which were then interlaced with withies (whippy willow growth). These weirs raised water depth over a given reach of a river or stream and by so doing extended the limit of navigation.

The first recorded civil engineers came to this country in AD45 with the arrival of the Romans. After not much more than a quarter of a century Romanization was settled with a system of forts and garrisons across the country, all being connected with an efficient highway system. In time the garrisons became prosperous cities and colonies; the significant point of this occurrence is the fact that the most important ones were sited on either tidal or river navigations, prominent examples being London, Gloucester, Lincoln, York, Chester, Exeter, Winchester, Rochester, Caerleon, Carmarthen and Colchester. Obviously navigation, even within a limited area, was a most important means of transport and communication; hence it is not surprising to find that the Roman engineers dug and built the first canals in this country. Some of the best and oldest known of these navigations are the cuts and improvements they made to connect the River Cam with the Bedfordshire Ouse and so to the Nene at Peterborough. From this town they constructed the Caer Dyke to connect with the River Witham at Lincoln, then on with the next obvious link to the Trent, which river it joined at the place we know today as Torksey.

In the last few years a lot of new information has come to light about Roman inland waterway transport, particularly in the north of the country on the Rivers Tees, Tyne and Coquet (thanks to the dedicated work carried out by that very sharp eyed and practical archaeologist, Raymond Selkirk). There is no doubt that the Romans carried out many waterway improvements and canalized rivers, over much of the country; however rivers delight in changing course and have power to destroy the works of man over a period of time which leaves ample scope for interpretation by waterway archaeologists. The basis of a belief that research needs to be carried out in this direction lies in two simple facts: firstly, whilst the Romans built good roads, their heavy wagons under highway laws of that period were not allowed to carry more than half a ton (in round figures) and would be pulled by anything up to ten oxen. Secondly, European style Roman barges carried about ten tons and required far less effort to move.

Since those early times the navigation of rivers steadily, although very slowly, improved, enabling barges to travel further. The River Severn was once navigable to Pool Quay near Welshpool; however this, the longest river in the United Kingdom, is not only subject to sudden and high floods, due both to heavy rain or melting snow cascading down from Wales, but also to that phenomenon the Severn Bore, created by the funnel shape of the estuary which induces the incoming tidal wave to increase in height to around four feet, and at certain stages of the equinox this can be more than doubled. The bore travels up to Gloucester where it subsides, though apparently an aftermath has been known to disturb the tideless waters as far upstream as Worcester. The barges of the Severn are known as 'trows' (rhyming with crow) and were designed to sail on the river in question; in early times they were square rigged but gradually took on a fore and aft ketch rig. When sailing conditions on the upper reaches became difficult they would be towed by gangs of men known as bow hauliers; the earliest indication of a horse towing path being proposed goes back to the very early 1760s.

The River Trent has been used for navigation from time immemorial, but the first Act of Parliament for keeping it navigable was passed in 1689, followed by improvements in 1783, then in 1794 an Act authorized the construction of locks and weirs; previously boatmen had carried on as best they could overcoming both the natural obstacles to navigation and those made by the proprietors of fishery weirs and mills. The river below Gainsborough is tidal and subject to the Eagre which is similar to, but less spectacular than the Severn Bore.

The River Humber, which connects the Rivers Ouse, Trent, Hull and Ancholme, is probably best known to inland waterway enthusiasts for its traditional commercial craft known as 'Humber keels'. They were square-rigged craft with a mast stepped in a tabernacle to facilitate lowering when negotiating bridges; they were provided with leeboards to assist progress when sailing into the wind. Capacity of these craft varied up to 100 tons, whereas trows had something like half that capacity. I understand there is a restored fully rigged Humber keel available for pleasure trips, whilst there are still a number of diesel powered versions around. Further up country another speciality was the Tyne keel.

The River Wye, together with its tributary the Lugg, were once navigable up to Hereford; it is likely that there were flash locks on the Wye in the seventeenth century: at the very beginning of the nineteenth century an Act was obtained to construct a horse towing path for some thirty miles below Hereford.

The earliest attempt to improve transport from Manchester to Liverpool goes back to around the 1660s when there were endeavours to secure an Act to make the rivers Irwell and Mersey navigable: the history of this is somewhat complicated but suffice it to say the navigation was opened in 1736, and was provided with a towpath to facilitate barge hauling by manpower.

In Norfolk the River Yare has borne commercial craft since the days of the Romans; dredging apart, no major works were carried out on this river until the nineteenth century. The popular trading craft of the Norfolk Broads in olden times was the Norfolk keel, to be superseded in due course by the now romantic 'Norfolk wherry'.

The great up-river trading craft of the Thames was the West Country Barge which goes back to medieval times; originally square-rigged, but in the later years of its existence it carried a spritsail rig. These barges were of varying sizes, the largest being 200 tonners. In the reign of George III, an Act was passed limiting these craft to a draught of 3 feet. The popular Thames sailing barge was evolved from the Thames lighter of the seventeenth century.

There were many commercial boats whose trading was in the main of local nature, such as the Newbury barges which traded down the Kennet to the Thames and the Guildford barges which made good use of the river Wey for Thames trading. On the Fens there were the Fen lighters traversing the middle level navigations so we can go on with Weaver flats, Liverpool wide boats and the subsequent development of steam and then diesel powered craft, with 'Tom Puddings' which were 35-ton capacity compartment coal boats towed in a train by a steam tug on the Aire and Calder Navigation. To describe the legality of non-tidal rivers I will quote from A.S. Wisdom's book, *The Law of Rivers and Watercourses* as follows:

Navigation on non-tidal rivers

The public have no right at common law to navigate on non-tidal inland waters, but a right to do so may be acquired by immemorial usage by the public, by dedication of riparian owners or under statute. A claim to establish a public right of navigation over a non-tidal stream must be treated as if it were a claim for a right of way on dry land, and the right thus acquired is simply a right of way; the public who have acquired by user the right to navigate on an inland water have no right of property.

With the building of the Bridgewater Canal in 1760 a network of canals steadily spread across the country; as most of these canals were constructed to carry craft of limited beam, so the narrow boat was developed (a craft 72 foot long with a beam of 7 foot). With the rapid development of canals it was not long before the major rivers of the country became inter-connected, thus bringing more commerce to riverside towns and trading centres. Although commercial traffic upon our waterways was adversely affected with the advent of railways it persisted until the late 1960s and in some areas to the early '70s, after which, with the exception of local pockets of trade, the decline in waterborne transport more or less coincided with the development of motorways.

Pleasure boating on our rivers in the generally accepted sense was under way early in the nineteenth century and grew rapidly in popularity, as we all know today. However, cruising on our canals was indeed a rare experience for private boat-owners until the late '50s when it began to take over from the once heavy traffic of working narrow boats. On reflection how glad I am that I enjoyed a considerable amount of canal travelling in the days of working waterways, besides the pleasure of knowing some of the boatmen and their families including 'Tubby'

Wilson and his wife who was always ready to welcome one aboard with a mug of tea. The Brays were really great folk; when my sons were approaching their teens Rose Bray advised me to give them a glass of Jumbo stout every day, this being her favourite tipple. The Ward family were a grand crew and sometimes came down to the Thames for us; whilst Jack Monk was a boatman par excellence, with his dog Bruce, also a great character and very capable poacher; yes the stories could fill a book. My son Tom sometimes crewed for Jack in his school holidays on the 'coal run' from the Atherstone collieries to the Jam 'Ole at Southall (that was Kearley and Tonge's jam factory). There was nothing Jack enjoyed more than beating his previous best time for this journey and excelled himself on every time-saving dodge that could possibly be used. One thing that struck one about the canals in those now far off days was the courtesy shown by the working boatmen; it was generally of an exemplary nature and that is more than you can say of many private boaters of the present age.

With the decline of canal traffic many of our man-made waterways fell into disrepair; some were closed and others were impassable. The fight to reclaim them as navigable routes was tremendous, but it was a battle well fought which is proved today by the extensive network of canals and rivers upon which we can cruise with pleasure, although without the spirit of pioneering, inasmuch that in the days when cruising on our canals was little practised, there were no facilities for fresh water, rubbish disposal, fuelling points and suchlike services that are nowadays taken for granted. Furthermore there were no detailed maps (other than O.S. publications for walkers) let alone specialized canal handbooks. One benefit of the cessation of regular commercial traffic has been the increase in wildlife, whilst particularly apparent has been the way in which plant growth has luxuriated.

At the moment our waterways are under the jurisdiction of various authorities and organizations, the catchment areas of England and Wales being administered by ten separate authorities, which are as follows: the Northumbrian, North West, Yorkshire, Severn-Trent, Anglian, Thames, Southern, Wessex, South West and Welsh Water. However navigation authorities do not fall into the same arrangement, for example Thames Water are responsible for the Thames but not the River Lee which comes within their catchment area; likewise Anglian, although acting as navigation authority for most of the rivers in their area, do not cover the Norfolk Broads, the Middle Level, or the River Cam. These anomalies, along with other problems, will no doubt be dealt with in due season with the formation of the National Rivers Authority which will be controlling river and navigational problems with the advent of the water industry being privatized.

Broadly speaking responsibility for our canal system rests upon the shoulders of the British Waterways Board which owns some 2,000 miles

Weed clearance on the River Nene. Elevator on left is stacking cut weed on bank; weedcutter is moored on inside of barge on right of picture.

of inland navigation, of which approximately 1,750 miles are classified as navigable, but those with narrow boats and suitable cruisers must content themselves with the fact that there are only 1,200 cruising miles, which includes the Rivers Severn, Trent, Lee, Stort, Weaver, Soar and Ure, for which British Waterways is the navigation authority.

The Norfolk Broads are administered by the Broads Authority, formerly the Great Yarmouth Port and Haven Commissioners. It is to be reorganized so that the Broads will be on a similar footing to a National Park with accompanying government grants. The Bill put forward received Royal Assent on April 1st, 1988, and it is expected that 'The New Broads Authority' will come into being in 1989.

If you keep and use a boat on your local stretch of water then licensing with the appropriate authority presents no problem. If however you wander round England on your boat, you will find that the number of individual licences to be obtained for such a voyage will be legion. Perhaps if and when a National Rivers Authority comes into being a unified system of licensing for boats will be introduced. At present a move is being made in this direction with Thames Water and British Waterways Board discussing a reciprocal licensing agreement to use one another's waterways without a visitors' licence.

In response to the poor condition of many canals, canal and navigation restoration groups, societies and organizations proliferate; they are all, without exception, carrying out a wonderful job of work.

One of the very early examples of restoration, which became a great success story, was the Lower Avon from the point where it joins the River Severn at Tewkesbury, winding round past Bredon Hill, through the old town of Pershore and so to Evesham. A group of determined and hardworking enthusiasts under the leadership of Douglas Barwell, O.B.E., formed the Lower Avon Navigation Trust in 1950 as a non-profitmaking company with the status of a charity. The trust, once formed, purchased the Navigation Works of the Lower Avon which had been permitted by the previous owners to fall into a state of complete dereliction. They then pledged to restore and maintain the locks, weirs, dams and sluices without which the river would revert to its natural state of a small muddy brook, useless to the angler, unnavigable to craft, and an eyesore to all who beheld it. The work of restoration was carried out by the trust's volunteer working parties who relied for finance for materials and equipment on donations made by the public and well wishers; here is a typical news item of the period: 'David Burlingham of the Trust announced that materials were on order for a new pair of upstream lock gates at Pershore Lock.' This was just one of the many statements that from time to time appeared in the press together with appeals for financial as well as physical help.

In the meantime the Upper Avon Trust, urged on by David Hutchings' fighting spirit, made the river navigable from Stratford-on-Avon down to Evesham, which achievement took five years, and the waterway was opened by the Queen Mother on June 1st, 1974. David Hutchings, M.B.E., was also responsible for restoring the Stratford-on-Avon Canal (connecting with the Grand Union Canal) which he successfully completed in time for opening by the Queen Mother in 1964. He is now battling to restore navigation on the higher Avon from Stratford to Warwick, where he plans to have a new junction with the Grand Union Canal.

Over a very wide front covering our waterway system as a whole, a really great champion was the late Graham Palmer, who in the 1960s was inspired by the *Daily Telegraph* campaign to restore our neglected, and sometimes forgotten, inland waterways. His enthusiasm, together with his great powers of persuasion in enlisting volunteers and help from various directions, led to the formation of the Waterways Recovery Group, to act as a co-ordinating force not centred on any particular scheme, but assisting local groups on any worthwhile restoration plans. Since then the WRG, as it is known, has progressed in a splendid manner: it has gained expertise, amassed an essential fund of knowledge, and not surprisingly it has accumulated a very useful pool of plant and equipment; it is moving with the times by having a radio network for direct contact with various sites. Sadly Graham's premature death occurred at a time when he was actively engaged on the restoration of the Montgomery Canal; as I write, I understand that the British Waterways Board have given their blessing to the idea that the new lock, of limited depth, that is to be built below Welsh Frankton in order to allow headroom beneath the lowered crossing of the main road (A5), be named after Graham Palmer.

The history of The Great Ouse, sometimes referred to as the Bedfordshire Ouse, makes interesting reading and a fascinating study; it also fell into dereliction, hence the founding in 1951 of the Great Ouse Restoration Society 'To further the restoration of the Great Ouse between Tempsford and Bedford as a navigable highway and its repair and maintenance in its restored condition and so preserve and develop the amenities of the river for the benefit of all people.' The society kept its pledge, consequently there is a fine river for all of us to enjoy.

The Hollingwood Branch of the Ashton Canal suffered badly from subsidence, due to coal mining; hence a different approach was made towards restoration by forming a series of what one might loosely term 'lagoons' for recreational purposes such as fishing, canoeing, model-boat sailing, and so on.

At the time of writing action has begun in the High Court over navigation on the River Derwent, which will be a test case, for Malton Town Council are seeking a declaration that a public right of navigation exists along the non-tidal stretches south of Malton. Malton's claim is being opposed by riverside landowners and the Yorkshire Wildlife Trust who fear pleasure boats will respectively interfere with the seclusion of their properties and disturb wildlife. The situation is a cause for great concern and the Inland Waterways Association is pressing hard with its 'Waterways for All' campaign, which aims to promote freedom of navigation.

One of the earliest canal battles was to save the Kennet and Avon as a through route from the Thames to the Severn; it was in 1950 when John Gould Ltd, carriers of Newbury, were honouring a formal contract with T. Harrison Chaplin Ltd, that the Docks and Inland Waterways Executive (forerunners of the British Waterways Board) closed the canal, so locking John Gould's narrow boats in at Newbury. The contract enabled John Gould Ltd to enter into litigation; the story is a long one leading up to the eventual formation of the Kennet and Avon Canal Trust; after years of fund-raising, sheer hard work from volunteers and masses of help from well-wishers, the ultimate dream will come to fruition in 1989 with the Kennet and Avon once again being a navigation connecting two great watersheds.

To my mind the conservation work on the River Stour is exemplary; the exclusion of powered craft has had a beneficial effect upon the flora, and how peaceful it is to scull along that river with the only noise being the happy rippling sounds as the bows of one's boat cut through the water. The River Stour Trust carries out yeoman work with which its Vice Chairman, John Marriage, is very much involved, so much so that his name is almost synonymous with the Stour. The Stour Trust owns Flatford Lock (painted by Constable in 'The Hay Wain') but the mill, dock etc., are National Trust property. The barge-building dock has, since Constable's time, gradually filled up with rubbish and silt; the Stour Trust has now excavated it to find that not only has it a brick floor but that lying on this was the remains of a lighter. (To those with an inquisitive mind I would add that the dock is drained via a pipe running under the river bed to an outlet at a lower level.) The trust is rightly proud of its Stour Barge which it raised and restored, the barge having lain on the river bed since the First World War. It also located and raised the remains of a steam barge. Great attention has been given to Sudbury Basin which includes the restoration of the old granary and subsequent conversion to a theatre. The trust had help from the Manpower Services Commission and also the United States Air Force Civil Engineering Squadron.

Energetic and hardworking enthusiasts are showing their determination in the restoration of the Rochdale Canal and its eventual re-connection with the rest of the country's canal system, the point of union being Sowerby Bridge, at the head of the Aire and Calder Canal. It was in 1961 that the late Lionel Munk, former Chairman of the Inland Waterways Association and founder of Maid Line Cruisers Ltd (later to become Maidboats Ltd) made a pioneering and publicity cruise to Sowerby Bridge from the Thames.

Up in Yorkshire plans are afoot to form a trust to look after the interests of the lovely River Ure and that other delectable river, the Yorkshire Ouse. Seemingly the body will be called the 'Yorkshire Ouse and Ure Navigation Trust'.

Across the country there are many schemes afoot, all with the same object in view – re-instatement of navigation. This in itself is excellent, but the wonderful opportunities that present themselves for conservation must not be overlooked in the quest for once again navigating boats on waterways that had become derelict. Restoration and conservation of waterways is not just the prerogative of those wishing to put old navigations back into use, for the British Trust for Conservation Volunteers is very actively engaged on the waterway and wetlands front; its interpretation of 'waterways' covers rivers, streams, ditches, canals, ponds, lakes and those lovely mystical founts of water we call springs. It regards 'wetlands' as areas that are covered with water, or are waterlogged for the major part of the year, such as marshes, bogs, swamps, wet grasslands and fens. And its aim is to conserve the flora and fauna of those areas, rather than provide a navigation route.

Most of our swamps have been drained, but possibly the best known – especially to bird watchers – is Minsmere in Suffolk. Tracts of peatland, where the water table is exceptionally high, do not dry out and are referred to as 'mires', and are hosts to various species of bog moss and acid loving growth, as can be observed in Cheshire and parts of Staffordshire, particularly when travelling on the Shropshire Union/Llangollen canals. Peat often dates as far back as the last Ice Age and due to its preservative qualities historic finds are sometimes made; also pollen which to the scientist yields a fund of information on past climatic conditions (over thousands of years) as well as plant distribution.

Fens are mires suited to the growth of plants that require alkaline conditions as can be witnessed after leaving the River Nene at Peterborough, dropping down to the Whittlesey Dike and navigating, below sea-level, the Fenland Waterways.

To some conservationists dredging is almost a dirty word. However if we are to maintain a really efficient land drainage system throughout the country and navigate our boats on appropriate waterways, then dredging is essential. In a river such as the non-tidal length of the river Thames, the amount of solid matter settling on the river bed under normal flow conditions amounts to slightly more than 1 ½ cwt per million gallons of water; furthermore that solid matter has nothing to do with man made pollution, it is purely a result of erosion and soil washed off the land. In times of flood and increased flows the amount quoted is considerably increased.

Whilst non-navigable rivers and streams are normally a haven for all forms of plant and wildlife, they also render an important service in carrying storm water besides acting as a receptacle for many a farmer's land drains. Consequently such watercourses require dredging or de-silting from time to time in order to remain efficient from the land drainage point of view. With the ever increasing demand for new houses, more motorways and factory estates, together with an increase in agricultural land drainage our waterways are having to take much greater quantities of water, so giving rise to an increase in the dredging, widening and sadly the straightening out of many a brook, stream or channel. In many cases this work has been, and to a certain extent still is, carried out in an unsympathetic manner with large hydraulic excavators mounted on 'go-anywhere' crawler tracks. With these machines gravel beds, beloved of fish for spawning, are ripped out; banks are cut back and graded so relieving them of all vegetation, but worst of all, in order to position the excavator on top of the bank as well as allowing manoeuvring space for the brute, the very trees whose roots hold the bank together are ripped out. When the work of so-called improvement has been carried out the banks are left barren, straight and a complete eyesore to man and presumably hell to nature in all its forms.

However, I am glad to say that authorities are now relenting inasmuch that they have devised methods for carrying out the work whereby the trees, or at least the vast majority of them, can be left in situ: the cutting back and grading of banks now follow easy curves rather than straight lines whilst the vegetation that is removed is not completely disposed of, for an adequate amount of rushes, reeds, meadow-sweet, hemp agrimony, purple loosestrife and such like herbage is put to one side for replanting as soon as a reasonable length of river has been cleaned. To those not experienced in the handling of machines it should be noted that a skilled excavator driver can place plants with his hydraulically actuated digging bucket as deftly as a gardener with a spade. But whichever method is employed the excavated material is deposited on the bank, sometimes levelled out, or quite often formed into a berm, or bank, to prevent flooding of adjacent land. With the enlightened method of cleaning out our watercourses the environment is protected whilst essential good drainage is maintained; to quote from 'The Brook' by Lord Tennyson, 'I come from haunts of coot and hern . . . and sparkle out among the fern'.

In the Kennet valley are peat deposits, which in the past were lifted, dried and burnt, the resultant ashes being used on the land as a fertilizer. In fact in the eighteenth and very early nineteenth centuries Newbury peat ashes were greatly prized by the market gardeners of Middlesex, so much so that there was regular barge traffic down the Kennet and on to the Thames to deliver this 'fertilizer' to various local wharves alongside the Middlesex bank of the river. The ancient Kennet Valley peat deposits may well be the outcome of the damming of streams by beavers in past time when these industrious animals were indigenous to this country. The peatlands of this country are another part of our heritage which is being depleted, ironically by a section of the community who are often conservationists at heart; I am of course referring to the tremendous amount of peat used by domestic gardeners besides horticulture generally. There could however be a change in the situation with the increase in the use of bark mulch.

'Acorn' working parties of the National Trust also take part in waterway conservation and reclamation from time to time; this work is of course confined to National Trust properties which have their fair share of streams, lakes and ornamental waters, besides the River Wey Navigation, which was left to them by the previous owner, the late Harry Stevens of Guildford, whose family were renowned not only for water transport but the building of superb and very beautiful barges.

It is good to see that quarry owners are taking a lively interest in their disused and flooded sites and transforming them into nature reserves and recreational centres for all forms of water sport.

Even dear old village ponds have been taking on a new lease of life thanks to the 'Save The Village Pond' campaign organized by the British Waterfowl Association and the Ford Motor Company.

Having outlined the main sources of activity regarding restoration and conservation of our inland waters, last but not least there is the Thames Heritage Trust which will receive attention when dealing with another matter (see pp. 53, 56).

2

The Water's Edge

From a river conservation point of view, the water's edge takes precedence in requiring efficient and sympathetic attention. This is the case over a wide variety of conditions, whether open countryside, public open space, private property and/or residential development, or an industrial site; the other variable is whether the water course is a wild, free-flowing river, or a controlled navigable waterway. Erosion of river banks when left to the hands of nature normally occurs as a result of peak flows, so often occasioned by extremely heavy rainfall, melting snow, rapid thaw or that wretched situation of torrential rain at the end of a hard spell before a thaw has really begun to make itself felt. Another factor determining flood conditions is the direction of gale force winds and also the effect of spring tides holding back land water as it enters an estuary. The worst of any peak flow and/or flooding is generally brought about by a combination of several or all of the above-mentioned factors.

In exposed areas prevailing winds can play erosive tricks with a bank at waterline; should the bank be composed of a light sandy loam, then wind-aggravated erosion can be very considerable; this particular phenomenon is often clearly apparent on lakes. If the waterspace concerned is used for fishing, or there is a riverside public footpath, then erosion is often made worse on an undermined bank by pressure from pedestrians or anglers who unwittingly induce subsidence by their weight or movements, thus upsetting the accepted shoreline.

On navigable waterways the above factors apply just the same, but erosion is aided and abetted (and so increased) by the wash from powered craft which in the height of the holiday season can be incessant for the greater part of the day; boat design plays an important part in this phenomenon (see p. 84). Emergent water plants growing alongside the bank will greatly help in absorbing and dissipating wave energy. On the subject of wash, which is now one of the greatest navigational problems, it is interesting to recall that the House of Commons publication, *Hansard*, of August 1884, was devoted to the report from the Select Committee on River Thames Preservation and I quote from one item in that report, as follows:–
'... it is also urged that the presence of steam launches, of late years in increased numbers, on the river adds greatly to the wear

To the right can be observed the amount of water drawn away from the bank by a fast moving boat; to the left can be seen the rebound of the churned-up foamy water as the boat passes on its way. Dark area under the grass is an undercut section, being the result of, firstly, the suction caused by the drawdown, and, secondly, the bombardment created by the incoming wave.

of the banks, and therewith to the destruction of the water plants that edge the river'. The committee was very far-sighted; the actual amount of damage by steam launches was minimal, but it was the beginning of the power boat era of which the results are now very obvious and are, or should be, of great concern to all who use, love and respect our waterways; for the demise of many of our riverbank emergent and aquatic plants is now reaching serious proportions in many areas. A further effect of that is the depletion of cover for fur and feather.

Erosion is often caused by 'toe-scour', that is, removal of material from the base of the bank by a combination of abrasion and corrasion; the former being material moved from the face of the bank by the action of moving water, whilst the latter is material removed by the rapid repetitive action of soil particles in suspension hitting the bank (in other words it is rather the same action as having a machine, or article, shot-blasted prior to being plated or painted). Other factors effecting erosion are strong or prevailing winds, as already mentioned; large objects borne down on a flood can cause superficial damage on impact with a bank, but this is negligible. Excess loading on a bank such as a car park, buildings or other structures are an open invitation to trouble if the bank has not been strengthened to take such a weight. Then I would reiterate that pedestrian traffic on the top of the bank, close to the water, can be a contributory factor. When dealing with this subject due consideration must also be given to the nature of both the bank and the river bed. Boats making heavy wash, either because they are travelling too fast, or because they are not designed for use in confined waters (worse still a combination of both factors), will, if not being navigated to suit the conditions, draw a copious amount of water away from the bank, and with it minute particles of material; then, as the boat moves forward there will be a rebound in the form of waves, which bombard the bank, so setting up toe-scour. The individual damage may be slight but collectively, say over a whole season, the result can be dramatic; for the undercutting of the bank as the toe gets washed away is considerable, and soon reaches the situation where the now cantilevered area of herbage falls into the river, to be in turn washed away. If there is a reasonably wide swath of emergent plants, i.e. reeds and rushes, growing alongside the bank, then the effect of the wash upon the bank will be greatly reduced. However, with the dredging of navigable waterways and the ever increasing number of power boats afloat, it is not surprising that in some areas reed beds are on the decline.

Planting emergent plants just off the riverbank will absorb and dissipate wave energy, to the extent that bank damage will be eliminated or drastically reduced. Plants such as reed mace *(Typha augustifolia)*, sweet flag *(Acorus calmus)*, bulrush *(Scirpus lacustris)* and common reed *(Phragmites lacustris)* are excellent for the purpose. However, they are liable to be damaged by anglers cutting a way through them; dredging the main channel steepens the sloping sides of the river bed, which can expose the rhizomes (roots) of the plants, thus making them vulnerable to damage by wash – the problems are endless. Establishing new reed beds can prove most difficult; one way is to make planting bays with timber or mesh containers made from a geotextile.

Of the plants mentioned, sweet flag is so called because when the foliage is bruised an aromatic scent pervades the air; it is a plant that was introduced to this country from Asia in the sixteenth to seventeenth century; forethought is needed when planting, for under certain conditions it can cause silting; although it establishes itself well, it is of a cussed nature and so often grows best where there is no bank to protect. Sweet flag has rhizomes which can float above the bed and anchor themselves down with thin, but tenacious and flexible, assemblage of roots. Consequently any rhizome, or part of one, that breaks off and floats down river, can rapidly start a new colony. Reed mace forms matted rhizomes with masses of intertwining fine roots coming from the base of every stem. The species exists very well in spite of tending to become loose after spells of exceptionally heavy wash. The common reed has long rhizomes which intertwine to form dense mats on the bed with fine, deeply anchored thread-like roots coming from the base of each stem; the outer edge of a bed of

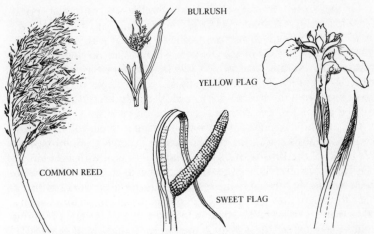

BULRUSH

YELLOW FLAG

COMMON REED

SWEET FLAG

common reed is subject to scour from both boat wash and very strong currents. Bulrush is very resistant to wave action, but the outer edge of the bed can suffer in the same way; its rhizomes, which are very short, are below the bed, and have close intertwining mats of roots, below and above the rhizomes.

Other plants to grow are the very lovely yellow flag *(Iris pseudacorus)*, which, with its glorious flowers overtopping the stiff leaves, makes a superb spectacle in spring and early summer. For functional purposes it is best incorporated with the previously mentioned plants; it does well on the lower edge of the bank or in very shallow water. *Phalaris*, the reed canary grass, does not grow in the water generally speaking, but enjoys a life on the very margin of the bank, for it appreciates an abundance of water at its feet.

This description of some of the most effective plants for protecting banks, particularly from the ravages of wash from powered craft, can help in many instances. However, great caution must be exercised on canals, particularly the narrow variety; for in shallow water with the minimum of flow, combined with silt that may be enriched from fertilizer washed off fields after heavy rain, growth can be terrific, so leading to the rapid blockage of a navigation.

It has already been mentioned that sweet flags can cause silting, but of course all our emergent plants, that is, those whose roots and lower parts actually live in water, and draw their nutrients from the soil of the river bed, succeed in accruing detritus, mainly because they are rich in cellulose: the dead foliage at the end of the season does not undergo complete decomposition, to the extent that as seasons come and go, the semi-decomposed material builds up, much to the delight of plants with a closely interwoven root system: the rising level of this matted material collects small particles with ease, so starting the silting up process.

On the Norfolk Broads, where holiday traffic is very heavy, it appears from historical information and old illustrations that Broadland rivers were at one time much narrower, due to thick growth on both sides. That was in the days of the Norfolk wherry, and no doubt its forerunner, the Norfolk keel, which was in use from Saxon times until early last century. In 1985 the only known example of such a craft was raised from the River Wensum, at Norwich. Preservation is being carried out and in due course she will be on view.

Back to the navigation: if the wash continues to cut too much bank away, so exposing peat, the situation could become grim, for basically the banks of the Broads rivers are composed of peat with a cladding of clay laid down after the ice age. Broadland has at an extremely slow rate been sinking, in relation to the sea, for centuries. Peat workings that go back to ancient time were flooded in the medieval era, so forming large lakes that we know as the Broads. In order that the farming fraternity could make use of the marshes, they were drained by digging dykes so as to lower the water table. But at the same time river banks had to be raised, and this task was carried out with clay raised from the bottom of the dykes, which in Norfolk are known as 'soke dykes' (in neighbouring Suffolk they are known as 'delphs'). The weight of clay gradually compresses the peat, upon which it is placed, and so the wall progressively subsides; the process of topping up river walls every few years continues. The bank between the clay wall and the river enjoys the characterful name of 'the rond'; erosion of the rond leads to the clay becoming unstable which in turn leads to major repair work to the bank rather than the growing of emergent plants.

Nature helps to stabilize banks by the growth of trees and shrubs, for root formation is such that it provides a wonderful soil stabilizing agent: man can assist by planting suitable species. Choice of specimens, if carrying out a planting scheme, can be legion; on natural banks choice is better confined to native species. The benefit of planting native trees and shrubs is the fact that they will happily host far more of our native butterflies, moths and creepy-crawlies, which in turn brings satisfaction to our bird life. Other considerations include, for example, on a towpath bank, ensuring that towing from the bank is no longer carried out. On the canals, under the jurisdiction of the British Waterways Board, tree planting must not be nearer to the water's edge than 12 feet (3 ½ metres). On non-navigable waterways (and a few navigable ones, too) some banks have to be kept perfectly clear, in order that dredging can be carried out with a land-based machine, whilst Thames Water stipulate that trees must be planted at least 26 feet (8 metres) back from the bank.

In time of summer floods, mature trees along the water's edge can be of inestimable value in disposal of water, for a tree in leaf requires a copious amount of water, but only a small amount is retained in the structure of the plant; the great bulk of water is used to carry dissolved

Traditional faggoting on the White River, St Austell, Cornwall.

minerals into the entire system. The water drawn in through the roots carries out its aforementioned duties through the trunk and branches to the leaves where it is transpired into the atmosphere. Transpiration is purely evaporation from the leaves, but on a gigantic scale, because on an average summer's day a large Huntingdon Willow, oak or similar sized old fellow can transpire up to 132 gallons (600 litres) of water vapour through its leaves every day.

Having outlined the way banks are damaged, the way nature tries to look after them when navigation does not interfere, and man's attempt to emulate nature, we now come to the point where man not only has to design a method of protecting the water's edge, but be capable of implementing his scheme. In the past, many a river had its bank protected with woven willow mattresses or bundles of faggots laid and held in place with stakes cut from a hedge or nearby hazel coppice. In Cornwall, where some of the fast flowing rivers carried a vast quantity of sediment from the China clay pits, the skilled river workers had the specialized know-how of placing their brushwood defences in such a way that they collected some of the sediment, enabling the finished product to become a first-class revetment. There are endless variations of the above methods; much depends on suitability of local materials; pegging wattle hurdles end to end along a sloping bank will do much to prevent erosion, and is a useful way round if basic material has to be brought in from a distance.

However, all this type of work, once so common to our forebears,

An example of faggoting.

is labour intensive; as modern economics and mechanical plant now hold the reins, traditional skills have become scarce and very much more expensive. However, subject to availability of materials and a good 'old hand' to take charge, most of these schemes can be viable for volunteer groups wishing to preserve certain sites as nature reserves and for fishing. For the new recruits on voluntary work, the simplest type of defence should be chosen, such as laying wattle hurdles (ready-made panels, woven from willow branches, that can be pegged down on a sloping bank). Cutting and driving large willow stakes at 5 to 6 ½ foot (1 ½ to 2 metre) centres, then cutting up the smaller willow branches to weave between the stakes to form a dense hedge is not recommended until plenty of experience and expertise has been gained. In fact 'hedge' is the type that millers sometimes erected as a weir, or in order to channel water to their mill.

3

Bank Protection

One of the best known methods of protecting a river or canal bank is campshedding, the original medium for this work being timber. The system consists of driving boards of the desired width and thickness – usually 9 x 2 inch (230 x 50 mm) into the river bed. The bottom end of the boards being cut with an adze to form a 'V' shape to facilitate driving. As it is difficult to obtain good penetration with such boards, square timbers, 4 x 4 inch (100 x 100 mm) or similar known as king piles, are driven at about 6 foot (2 metre) centres. These piles are pointed and if the bed is hard they are shod with steel caps: they are

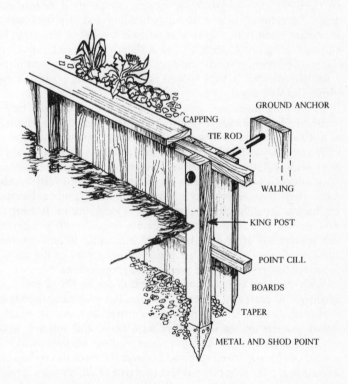

Typical cross-section of timber campshedding.

31

then driven a few inches in advance of the sheathing boards in order to leave room for a horizontal timber to run along the upper face of the sheathing to form a waling (sometimes spelt 'whaling') whilst a similar timber would run along the bottom to form a point cill; as it is difficult to get good penetration of the bed with sheathing boards, the point cill prevents them from 'toeing out', that is moving out into the river at their bottom ends in the event of any scouring or movement of the river bed. From the upper ends of the king piles, steel tie rods of approximately ¾ inch (20 mm) bar are taken back to ground anchors driven into solid bank. Sometimes blocks of concrete known as 'deadmen' are used for anchoring, but they tend to defeat the object of the exercise because the ground is inclined to be weakened in the course of excavating to make room for the concrete. Furthermore, with the end of the tie rod being bent over to grip into the concrete it precludes any tensioning of the rod; although threaded at both ends, the main adjustment to the rod is best made inboard where the rod passes through the ground anchor which at one time would have been a hefty piece of timber but nowadays is a section of steel pile, the length being dependent on local factors such as ground condition, height of campshedding and depth of water. An important point is to ensure that tie rods are not all the same length, so positioning of the anchor piles is slightly staggered, thus obviating the possibility of ground cleavage. If the anchor piles were driven in a straight line, the strain imposed upon them could possibly cause the ground to split open.

In the past, pitch pine was a very good and much used timber for campshedding; nowadays really good quality timber, in long lengths, is not easy to obtain, as well as being very expensive. Home grown elm, in the days when it was freely available, was used quite widely for river work and was best if always immersed; elm was most satisfactory on a north facing bank, for it never stood up well to dry conditions, particularly if it was subject to direct sunlight; another disadvantage of elm was the difficulty of obtaining it in long lengths. If using timber nowadays it is best to have it pressure treated with preservative to the appropriate British Standards Specification for marine timbers; however, first of all one must check the suitability of the timber, for some species reject, or will not absorb, preservatives.

With the high cost of timber, combined with the shortage of top quality, well seasoned material, and the fact that campshedding with timber tends to be labour-intensive, alternatives had to be sought. But before leaving timber work there have been, and still are, instances where the bank is low and the water shallow, so that point cill and waling can be dispensed with and horizontal boards can be laid behind, and affixed to the king piles. Whichever type of timber work is used, it is always finished off with a capping board; this being wide enough to cover the combined width of king pile, waling (if used) and sheathing,

Campshedding with timbers laid horizontally.

the main point of fixing the capping being to the top of king piles.

Originally, interlocking steel sheets were produced for contractors engaged on temporary works such as supporting the sides of deep trenches dug for the laying of pipes. In 1962, at a site near Staines, the then popular M7A style of sheets was used for what is believed to be the first example of campshedding a bank with this material. The outcome of the work was that it was an instant success, which, with a few modifications, soon became general practice. Unlike a timber frontage, king piles and point cill are superfluous, for the steel can be driven with a pile driver, or better still with a standard pneumatic sheeting hammer, so ensuring really good penetration of the river bed. A waling is very necessary in order to provide lateral stability and even out the tensioning of tie rods. Waling thus became a steel member, usually of angle section. However, although in theory it should be at the front of the sheets, set a little way down from the top edge, it is far better for it to be at the back, not only for aesthetic reasons but to allow a clean face upon which an 8 x 2 inch (200 x 50 mm) or similar timber rubbing strake can be fixed. This strake is 'kind' for boats coming alongside, whilst providing a finished appearance. Steel work can be galvanized, so giving longer life but can look shiny for up to twelve months until it has weathered; if the freeboard is low and

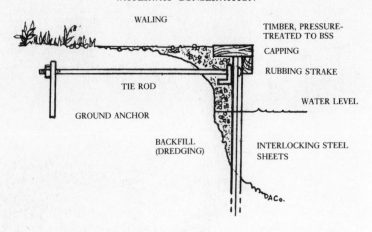

Typical cross-section of steel campshedding

the campshedding is frequently wetted, by wash or a prevailing wind blowing water on to it, it will soon be camouflaged with algae and other minute growth. It is customary to finish the work with a timber capping. Tie rods are spaced at around 8 foot (2 ½ metre) centres or closer as circumstances dictate. Sheeting should not be confused with piling; the former, as will have been observed, is virtually a greatly improved substitute for timber. Piling is of a vastly greater thickness and all-round dimensions, which can be driven to considerable depth and can be cantilevered where circumstances, or space, do not allow the fitting of waling, tie rods, and anchors.

For the record, it should be mentioned that the smooth surface of a campshedded bank increases the speed of the water flow: this can cause a destructive eddy at the downstream end of the new work if it is not properly terminated. A word about the preservation of timber; some people seem to get very worried in case impregnated chemicals leach out when wood happens to be immersed in a river or waterway. Providing the treatment conforms with the appropriate British Standards Specification, there is no fear of damage to fish, plants or wildlife in general. The same comments also apply to the majority of metal protective paints and coatings used on steelwork.

Over the years various materials have been used for campshedding, one of the early alternatives being concrete piles; on the canals these were widely used by the then newly formed Grand Union Canal Company way back in the 1920s and '30s, when our canal system was, of course, in the hands of free enterprise. The piles were made to a very high standard and driven to give copious penetration of the bed; they were usually finished with a concrete capping beam. In many areas of the Grand Union Canal system this piling is still giving yeoman

British Waterways maintenance gang pitching and driving concrete piles way back in the late 1950s on the Oxford Canal.

service; it is easy to identify because at regular intervals one can see piles that have figures moulded in to the upper face; these denote depth of penetration, whilst figures preceded with the initials 'DD' indicate the original dredged depth of the canal at that point.

After the war, with the nationalization of canals and the formation of the British Waterways Board, coupled with the shortage of steel, concrete piles once more came into fashion: to overcome with the lack of maintenance during the war, British Waterways established seven canal-side factories throughout the waterway system for the production of these piles, which by 1960 had reached an output of 130,000 units a year. They were heavy and cumbersome and not the easiest of things to drive, in spite of being chisel-shaped at the bottom. A great snag was bonus schemes; the lads in the casting shop, in order to meet or improve upon their target figure, sometimes became a little slap-dash, which generally resulted in the tops of the piles being distorted, so making it difficult to drive them plumb and true. This brought unhappiness to the pile-driving gangs who, with the variations encountered, found it difficult on some occasions to meet *their* bonus targets. These concrete piles had an external waling which generally consisted of lengths of old railway line; holes in the piles for bolting this in place and also for inserting tie rods were made in the mould shop.

Since those days private enterprise has experimented with concrete piles, one type being so-called 'lightweight' ferro-concrete and the other two (there may have been other attempts as well) were of glass reinforced concrete; admittedly the glass reinforced variety were relatively light and drove well, furthermore one pattern had the great advantage over other concrete products, inasmuch that they were interlocking, so making them similar to their steel counterparts. Unfortunately, these interlocks were so loose that sheets could 'wander' as they were being driven. Another disadvantage was that keeping the sheets upright increased the working hours per given run.

With the basic cost of these units being well in excess of steel, they were ruled out on economic grounds. Mind you, they required no paint or treatment, weathered well and were aesthetically pleasing as far as 'hard' waterside landscaping is concerned.

When it comes to revetments (bank facings), the most widely used medium is hessian bags filled with concrete. They first became popular on the Thames in the late 18th century with the need for towpaths (in olden times often referred to as 'bargewalks'). Due to the introduction of horse towing, the banks had to be strengthened to take the traffic imposed upon them. Timber campshedding was the standard practice, but at that time there was little imported timber and also a shortage of quality home-grown material. This fact is very evident when reading reports of finance committees, such as: '. . . fir piles, rails and planks are not lasting above 7 to 8 years'. Towpaths were invariably built up with gravel, which, subject to the nature of the river bed, would be dredged from alongside the bank; where the bed did not yield any, the gravel would have to be brought from another reach by barge. So with timber being in short supply and of poor quality, and necessity being the mother of invention, in comes cement to mix with the ballast, and hessian bags to hold the mixed concrete; after ensuring that there is a sound footing to take the weight of bags filled with dry concrete (which readily sets as it soaks up water from the river), the bags have to be lowered into place to take up the position of 'headers' and 'stretchers' – that is, bags laid alternately lengthwise and crosswise. They need to be laid to form a series of narrow steps so that the finished revetment has a batter, that is, a face that slopes back at a slight angle from bottom to top. Obviously bagwork (as it is called) is exceedingly ugly, but worse still, it inhibits the growth of plants, which in turn, means no cover for wildlife. In spite of this, some authorities still persist in using bags; furthermore some council officers who are most particular about laying adequate footings for walls and buildings seem to think that a bag revetment will stay in place, provided it is properly laid, regardless of the nature of the river bed. If it is really necessary to

Concrete bag revetment on the Thames.

build a revetment of concrete-filled bags, it is essential to have an intimate knowledge of the river bed in question; if it is not known, a very thorough survey is obligatory. The mass weight of concrete bags is a factor that should never be overlooked, however well they are laid. There are times when there may be slight crevices between some bags, so it is a wise precaution to lay a membrane such as 'Typar' or 'Terram' at the back of them, which allows water to seep through whilst retaining the fine particles in the backfill.

Mass concrete, other than in exceptional circumstances, is best avoided; not only because of its incongruous appearance, but a solid revetment of this material does not allow free drainage of the bank, and due to its unyielding nature, ground conditions must be stable and more than adequate footings must be provided.

To return to the question of sound footings for bag revetment, let me say that a river bed can vary considerably; sometimes a gravel bed can be extremely hard, just as though nature had graded, laid and consolidated the gravel as if it were Macadam laying his early roads, but it can be deceptive; hard gravel can be overlaying sand, then there are reaches where on one side of the river is superb gravel forming a perfect punting course, while the opposite side is soft clay. Chalk forms a good bed, but sometimes this can suddenly run into an area of mud. A classic case I remember is of a 6-foot (1.8-metre) wide

A typical example of cracked and slipping concrete as a result of underpinning.

jetty projecting at right angles to the bank for a length of 30 feet (9 metres). Supporting piles were driven at about 7-foot (2-metre) centres on both sides. All the piles on the left hand (upstream) side were driven into hard ballast whilst all the piles on the right hand (downstream) side had to be considerably longer due to the bed having changed in nature to clay. The most difficult bed to deal with is rock, but in the specialized trade there are a few techniques to help solve some of the problems involved.

In the 1950s and early '60s British Waterways developed a scheme for revetting towpath banks with concrete on the Shropshire Union Canal. They used a barge-mounted excavator to dig a trench down to consolidated ground, a little inboard of existing bank line; conventional plywood shuttering was erected and then concrete was placed, the aggregate and mixer being on an adjacent barge; whilst concreting was in progress the excavator would be trenching ahead, then shuttering would be 'leap frogged' and so the process would steadily continue. All very sound and sturdy, but of course it ruined the bankside beauty for quite a time, whilst nature was trying hard to re-assert itself.

Pre-fabricated concrete sections are available for bank protection work; it can hardly be said that they add charm to a waterway, but they do have their uses, particularly when a watercourse is assigned the task of carrying stormwater from a nearby motorway or a similar

Two pictures of experimental British Waterways bank protection work on the Shropshire Union Canal. Excavator cuts a channel between old bank and towpath, shuttering is placed in sides of trench into which concrete is poured. On completion, back of wall is filled to give a good towpath, earth in front is tidied up so that plants can grow in front of the concrete revetment. (1960)

Porcupine blocks: proprietary and very versatile walling system. The splined blocks allow curves and angles to be formed, while suitable spaces can be left for planting purposes.

situation. These sections can be in a 'crib' or open grid style which allows the free growth of shrubs and plants as well as small trees; some of these slabs are of an interlocking nature which can cope with water flows up to 3.0m/second at slopes of 2: 3 or less. Then there are 'Monoslabs' with smallish pockets through which grass can grow, so giving a pleasing overall appearance.

A revolutionary and very versatile concrete retaining wall system has been produced by a firm at King's Lynn; the product in question enjoys the trade name of 'Porcupine'. The concrete block sections have interlocking splines so providing stability and strength without the need for mortar. It can be laid on firm ground or bed by unskilled labour and can form a variety of different angles, shapes and facings, whilst it is possible to take curves as well. Furthermore, spaces can be arranged for planting.

At about the time we first started using interlocking steel sheets, specially shaped asbestos panels were being tested as a bank protection material in the United States (where the term 'bulkheading' is the equivalent of our 'campshedding'). They were successful with their trials and before long 'Unibank' sheets, as they were called, were being made in this country, with other manufacturers bringing out

Concrete grass paviors, typical of the Monoslab range, which give excellent bank protection, while allowing freedom of growth.

their respective alternative designs. The general method of using this material was the same as when sheathing with timber, but after a time it was found better, cheaper and quicker to use galvanized steel tube for king-piles, point cill and waling. As labour costs rose its demise was in sight and was finally brought about when Mabey and Johnson introduced a range of lightweight steel sheeting, including the M5 which proved cheaper per square foot than asbestos. Driving asbestos into a very firm river bed required particular techniques combined with custom-made driving equipment.

On the Fens around Ely – Earith and Denver in particular – the Anglian Water Authority use asbestos cement sheets on a grand scale for bank protection work. Due to the soft peaty nature of the bed, driving is pretty easy, so they cantilever the sheets by driving two-thirds of them into the bed; by so doing they are able to dispense with king piles, tie rods, walings and point cill. The finished job is effective but hardly pleasing.

41

Stone-filled Maccaferri gabions on M11 steel piling, protecting a high bank on a Gloucestershire flood relief channel.

The revetment par excellence is, no doubt, the one built with gabions. Most gabions are rectangular containers woven from heavy gauge steel wire mesh; they are strengthened by selvedges of heavier wire, as well as having mesh diaphragms which divide the containers into 1 metre compartments. Most gabions are available in a range of sizes from 1 to 4 metres long by 1 metre deep by .05 or 1 metre deep. There are also shallow units 6 metres long x 2 metres wide which are aptly named 'mattress gabions'. Normally the wire is galvanized before weaving either box or mattress gabions; as an extra long life precaution, or for use in polluted waters, they can be PVC coated. They are delivered in flat packs and easily opened out and assembled on site; once positioned, the individual sections can then be wired together to form the basis of the desired anti-erosion structure. Filling is then carried out, either by hand or with a suitable hydraulic digger, using quarried stone, gravel rejects or similar, providing the size is in the 125 – 200 mm range; after filling, the lid is pulled over and stretched into place before being wired down and so the process is repeated. Gabions made of welded mesh are available; however, the woven ones as described are far superior, for their flexibility allows them to yield, without loss of strength, to changing ground conditions. They are permeable, therefore no provision has to be made for pressure relief; they weather well and growth soon establishes itself. As well as being used for revetment work they are ideal for building weirs, dams and spillways. For the latter the mattress-type gabion can prove indispensable.

On a concrete spillway undercutting often occurs at the toe and carries on until the whole apron is undermined; with a mattress gabion, undercutting simply allows the toe to curl downwards and is thus self-sealing. The use of gabions tends to be regional, for if suitable stone or aggregate has to be brought in from afar, the cost can be such that the project is rendered uneconomic. In some instances graded crushed concrete can be used, but continuity of supplies can be a problem.

Where natural stone is freely available, and the river concerned is shallow, it can be used to advantage in building revetments that have warmth and character, be the stone freshly quarried or well weathered. The finished job usually has plenty of natural cracks and crevices both above and below water, so providing habitats for various forms of wildlife; then, too, silt that collects in crannies provides a root-hold for plant life. That bright little fellow with the yellow breast, the grey wagtail, is a great one for nest building in the crevices of rock. The biggest drawback with building stone revetments is the cost of handling the material on site, let alone any transport expenses that may be involved.

On the canals, where initial building with stone could be carried out in the dry, whilst for later maintenance work the pound could always be drained, the use of this material was widely used when there was an abundance of stone close at hand. Fine examples of really beautiful stonework can be appreciated on parts of the Southern Oxford canal, where the warm old stone looks so homely – rather akin to Cotswold walling. Then on the northern section of the Oxford Canal there are some stone revetted banks reclining at an angle of about 45º. On the Leeds and Liverpool canal there is superb stone block walling, complete with stone capping. As an absolute contrast there are a few sections of bankside in the Birmingham area where large square cut blocks of coal have been used: nothing like using local material! The Bridgewater Canal takes on a different look with its sides being of red sandstone blocks; admittedly with the years of weathering and the pollution of the past, they often look more black than pink.

Travelling up the Shropshire Union Canal is a beautiful experience, especially where the canal passes through deep, well wooded cuttings, some of which are hewn from soft pink sandstone, which gives a warm background to so much lush foliage. On approaching Chester one can anticipate the pleasure of mooring against sturdy stonework that was constructed by the Romans, for at this point the 'Shroppie', when being dug, made use of a former Roman Dyke; Chester Lock is hewn out of solid rock.

According to siting of quarries, canal builders (i.e. 'navvies') sometimes changed over to bricks, if that commodity was close at hand. When the Staffordshire and Worcestershire canal was built, the engineers made good use of the stone that was in situ, whilst leaving some fascinating features, such as a bold and striking outcrop at Kinver.

On rivers, from time to time, one sees revetments of brick, and occasionally of stone; most of these are in fairly deep water, particularly town and former commercial wharves. Many a holiday maker has been puzzled as to how footings could have been made for such a heavy mass rising out of the water; well, the answer is that there are no conventional footings, for in most cases the weight of the wall is taken by a massive timber campshedding with king piles as big as 12 inches (300 mm) square, closely spaced and with an equally massive waling. Timber for this type of work was, almost without exception, greenheart; this is an extremely hard wood with fantastic durability, making it the perfect material for lock gates, underwater structures, piles and such like marine structures. The majority of greenheart, known botanically as *Ocotea rubra*, comes from the forests of Guyana.

There is now a limited revival in building both brick and stone revetments that appear to rise up from the river bed: in fact they are built on footings behind a toe of steel campshedding.

A modern method of revetting is the use of geotextiles which come in various types from a number of different manufacturers; some are in the form of a relatively simple mesh that rolls out easily, does not kink and can be pegged down on to a once eroded area that has been reclaimed with dredgings. In this direction there are a number of proprietary products that can prove most useful in stabilizing the infill, whilst grass and plants can grow through it without any problem. After it is laid and pegged it is prudent to give it a dressing or 'blinding' of soil or silt before sowing grass or wild flowers; in any event if either anglers or cattle frequent the area it should be fenced off until the infill has settled and grass and plants established. A more sophisticated (and expensive) material is a product from Holland, known as 'Enkamat'. It is a thick matting of crinkly high-tenacity nylon threads which are welded where they cross; the air space between the threads amounts to 90% of the total mass, so when laid seed can, and should be sown, before giving the whole area a dressing of soil. The root-like formation of Enkamat protects the top layer of soil, so preventing seeds and small plants from being blown or washed away; as they become established, matting and plant growth become homogeneous, with excellent anchorage into the soil below, so providing an extremely resilient protection system that is in the best interests of conservation. The above method can be used in

WATER
LEVEL

TOE OF ENKAMAT
FACTORY FILLED WITH
ASPHALT

Enkamat. A three-dimensional material, which, after laying, leaves plenty of room for the growth of riverside herbage. In this case it has been laid with a toe of factory-filled asphalt.

conjunction with a 'toe' of campshedding, or in some circumstances another type of Enkamat can be used if the bottom edge is going right down to the river bed; it is known as Enkamat 'A' and can either be completely filled or just the part to be immersed can be filled with bitumen bound permeable gravel. The filling operation is carried out in the factory, so there is no messy site problem to contend with.

When the courses of various rivers and streams have to be diverted in making room for a new motorway, Enkamat has really come into its own, not only in providing a sound engineering job but giving a finished appearance which in a matter of months looks completely natural. Enkamat is easy enough to handle when there is plenty of room to manipulate the very long rolls of material and manoeuvre a large hydraulic excavator of the 'Hymac' type. Unfortunately, as yet, size of the rolls has not been scaled down so that Enkamat can be used on renovation work where access to site is difficult and at the best only approachable with a small, shallow-draught, narrow beam workboat with a very small hydraulic digger.

The latest development is a geotextile that can be used for vertical revetments; it provides excellent erosion control for quite a small outlay, furthermore it is not labour intensive and is easy to handle. It is a prefabricated double-weave fabric made of ultra-violet-inhibited

In the City of Guildford, the requirement for the public open space on the bank of the River Wey was that it should look as natural as possible. It was campshedded with steel to normal water level, thereafter the bank was protected with Enkamat and duly sown with a grass/wild seed mixture.

stabilized monofilament yarns, with sleeves at regular intervals through which stakes are positioned; the fabric is then stretched taut using a Tirfor or similar handwinch, before driving the stakes home. Machine-turned posts, complete with point and chamfered tops are ideal for this operation, they can be purchased already pressure-treated with preservative to the requisite British Standards Specification. In the interest of natural surroundings, this material, called 'Nicospan', is ideal for it allows vegetation to grow freely. Another good point is that it can follow pleasing curves, so obviating dead straight sides like a drainage channel; and by the way, machine-turned posts are not only very good value for money, but are so easy to handle that there is a valuable spin-off in the saving of labour costs. At the moment experiments are afoot using biodegradable mats impregnated with grass and/or appropriate wild flower seed mixture. These 'mats' are placed at the back of the Nicospan, starting at water level, as backfilling progresses.

Another fabric is 'Nicolon' which has inbuilt pockets, the lower ones being used to take stone or rubble to hold the fabric on the bed whilst the upper pockets are for the positioning of plants; pioneer work with this material was carried out by the British Waterways Board back in 1982. It provides a technique allowing the development of natural plant cover which in turn encourages a wide range of wildlife along the bank of a canal whilst providing the bank with protection against scour. The problem with Nicolon is that the filling of the pockets can

Nicolon.

The river bank of the Home Park, Windsor; appreciation for the requirements of conservation and a duty to ensure that waterside work is environmentally pleasant are factors that are conspicuous by their absence in this otherwise delightful reach of the Thames.

47

be a fiddly and time-consuming job; besides which there are quite a few components to deal with, not forgetting the species of plants; even with a well organized workboat this can become a major task when working in remote areas.

Machine-turned timber, pressure-treated to British Standards Specificiations for lumber immersed in water, can provide a very pleasing revetment where the bank is fairly low and the water relatively shallow by driving these poles side by side into the bed; being machine-turned they fit snugly together; furthermore, they can be purchased with a chamfered top and pointed ends. Then too, they are available as half-round poles, which in some situations are quite satisfactory and more economical to use. This timber, a product of lumber mills in the heart of Worcestershire, provides a new dimension for jetties, river structures and general landscaping. It made its debut for jetty construction in 1987 when providing new facilities for the London River Yacht Club.

For the sealing and waterproofing of artificial lakes, reservoirs and ponds there are various proprietary materials and methods available; a very well known natural product is 'Bentonite', which is widely used in the civil engineering field for the construction of diaphragm style earth dams whilst it is also used for sealing and waterproofing lake beds and other areas where water retention is required. Considerable expertise and experience is required in using this material, with which a first-class and natural-looking job can be created. Bentonite comes as a dry white powder which on contact with water enables the mineral particles to swell to about ten times their own size, after which the material forms an impermeable gel. Bentonite comes from America; in fact it is mined in Montana and owes its name to the place of origin, Fort Benton in that state. (To digress I would mention that Fort Benton is situated 3,000 miles up the Missouri River which has earned that town the soubriquet the 'World's Innermost Port'. In the era of large paddle steamers those intrepid vessels, commonly referred to as 'mountain boats' not only had to contend with the elements, the whims and difficulties of the Missouri, but also the Indians. A well known steamboating man of last century, Captain Leathers, was once asked how he got his boat over the shallows on his way to Fort Benton; his simple reply was 'I just kept a 'shovin'.!)

Fuller's Earth, which is excavated from various sites in this country, is related to Bentonite; so much so that after processing it can be turned into a product bearing the trade name 'Brebent' which can be used in the same way as Bentonite.

4

The Water Itself

Pollution is not a new invention: it has been going on since at least the industrial revolution, when many canals were so bad that horses could not drink from them. Causes range from industrial discharge, carelessness on the farm, to man's insatiable habit of throwing his trash into the nearest river or stream (failing that, from the bridge top of a convenient canal). With so many motorways in existence, or being built, the surface drainage from these highways, along with ordinary roads, can cause damage to our rivers and streams. Whilst rainwater is comparatively clean when it falls upon a road, it can be an unpleasant liquid by the time it reaches a watercourse, having collected oil, salt and traces of noxious substances from the road surface. In some areas river levels now appear to be fluctuating wildly and running often with less velocity; river authorities seem aware of the problems, but there is a vast equation to resolve: the increasing requirement for water in industry and agriculture together with man's ever increasing demand for an even better standard of living, versus a well oxygenated river and a healthy aquatic environment.

To many the word pollution is associated with toxic materials being dumped or thrown into a river or watercourse, when in fact the main trouble is usually caused by an excess of nutrients entering the water. However a flowing river whose water tumbles over natural falls or man-made weirs obtains a goodly quantity of oxygen on its way downstream and such rivers are to a large extent self-cleansing. To anyone who regularly swims in a river the oxygen content is usually apparent by the 'feel' of the water, whilst a good indication of the quality of the water in a river or stream is the amount, and variety, of wildlife to be seen, together with the fish population. By the same token the quality and variety of plant life will tell its own story; plants also play their part in the oxygen cycle. Remember too that cold water holds more dissolved oxygen than warm water, this again being apparent when swimming. I have noticed that the River Trent from a point where it is joined by the River Soar is really warm – even in cold weather – due no doubt to the discharge of cooling water from power stations, which makes an early morning swim comparable to a hot bath. Industrial pollution in some areas is extremely bad; one example that comes to mind is the Yorkshire River Rother; companies proved to be allowing noxious waste to enter the river have been fined. However, one wonders if a fine, however heavy, could be a cheap solution for a large industrial concern to its disposal problem. Possibly the fine would be best invested in a river improvement scheme and the firms involved should participate in water purity management.

Turning to agriculture: excess nitrogen seems to be the main worry at the time of writing. Farmers are blamed for excessive use of nitrogenous fertilizers which gradually seep into the water table or are washed off the land in times of heavy rain to contaminate streams and rivers. Remember, too, that ploughed up grassland does release, albeit slowly, a fair quantity of nitrogen and for that matter a considerable amount of nitrate leaching from agricultural land comes from the breakdown of organic matter. It would appear, however, that the government is preparing legislation to control the use of nitrates and also of certain pesticides; by the time this book is published it may be that new powers will have been introduced that will curtail the use of certain conventional modern farming practices.

The use of pesticides, fungicides and herbicides also comes in for criticism; often quite rightly, but of course it is easy to pass judgement when one's living is not dependent on the growing of first-class crops. However, both British Rail and local authorities must take their share of the blame for any possible build-up of herbicides. Silage (which is becoming more popular now than hay as a winter fodder) is prepared by the storing and fermenting of grass and green forage in a pit or silo. The liquid produced during fermentation may look like an innocuous plant by-product, but a teaspoonful of this fluid is equivalent to a quart of raw sewage: hence every precaution has to be taken to avert seepage into a watercourse and in this direction every effort is being made, generally at great expense to the landowner or farmer: some systems have been developed whereby the liquor is stored for use as a liquid fertilizer at a later date.

A joint report by the Water Authorities Association and the Ministry of Agriculture, put forward some time ago, indicated that farm silage and slurry was a pollutant of many watercourses. The National Farmers' Union commenting on the report said there was evidence that in general farmers were acting responsibly and co-operating with water authorities; the right course for the authorities was first to advise and help and prosecute only if pollution continued. Since then the Severn Trent Water Authority has made an announcement to the effect that they will make an aware to the livestock farmer in the Severn-Trent region who, in the opinion of the judges, has done most to prevent and control pollution on his farm within the constraints of successful commercial farming. The first prize is a trophy plus £400 in cash and second price £250.

Plant breeders are currently working on a new strain of wheat whose physiology like that of leguminous plants will be able to extract nitrogen from the air, and besides using part for its own growth it will leave the soil richer in nitrogenous constituents than before. This would help to limit the amount of nitrogenous fertilizer to be put on the land. Other sources of nitrate are sewage, sewage sludge and, believe it or not, thunderstorms; in summer time I expect most of us, at sometime or another, have remarked on the greenness of the lawn after a good old thunderstorm.

If sewage or sewage sludge is in excess in water, or finds its way into a watercourse that is not well oxygenated, then the results can be deleterious. The reason for the spate of recent problems is, no doubt, the very rapid development of residential estates in the last few years, coupled with the fact that our older sewage works have been hard pressed to keep pace with the demand. Again recent reports indicate that finance is coming forward for the improvement, and, where required, the modernization of existing sewage works besides the building of new ones. The Anglian Water Authority was the first in the field with a new and natural method of treating sewage. The installation was made close to the River Bure and provides low cost treatment whilst contributing towards improved water quality in the Broads area. Basically the method consists of constructing a water-tight pan, which, having been covered with a layer of soil, is planted up with reeds; sewage, having been de-gritted and comminuted, is directed down a channel which enters the top end of the reed bed, the upper metre or so being covered with gravel to encourage even distribution of the inflow. The reeds act as a biological filter. The sewage passes horizontally through the bed, mainly below its surface; the reeds transfer oxygen to the soil through their hollow stems and rhizomes, so stimulating the growth of bacteria to break down the sewage. This system is known as RZM, which stands for 'root zone method' and it is understood that RZM can reduce both installation and operating costs dramatically. The system was first developed in Germany where it is proving most successful; furthermore there is a bonus with the system inasmuch that phosphate is removed from the sewage.

It is good to see individuals and groups dealing with problems or potential hazards in a practical way; in this direction the Residential Boat Owners' Association has spent time and care in researching and testing a range of biodegradeable cleansing agents in an effort to help maintain the purity of our rivers and waterways. They located one chain of health shops (Holland and Barrett) that can supply some of their requirements and are currently looking into the possibility of importing other specialities from Germany.

I started off with a comment about the dumping of trash into watercourses of all kinds; I should mention that some riverside gardeners are not averse to allowing grass mowings and other garden rubbish to slip into the water, whilst some make good use of a flood for despatching unwanted goods down river. Then there is the occasional boat owner who, on changing his engine oil, pours the old gunge into an empty drum which he craftily sinks in deep water; with the passage of time the drum starts to leak and so a tiny oil slick starts off. In the daily press we read worldwide news about pollution of the atmosphere from vehicle exhaust fumes, but never a word about boats on inland waters.

As an aside, interesting experiments are being carried out by Thames Water in the use of Nile pike, a fish from Africa, for testing the purity of water. This pike is sometimes referred to as an 'electric' fish because, due to its absence of eyesight, it sends out 400 electric pulses a minute to navigate and locate food. If the quality of the water deteriorates the pike is affected and changes the frequency of its electric pulses.

Another form of pollution is the result of bad manners and complete lack of self-discipline; I am of course referring to the remains left behind by picknickers, fishermen and sometimes boating parties. Beer and Cola cans with their tiny triangular openings are a death trap for one of our loveliest little mammals, the water shrew, who is but 3 inches (7 ½ cm) long with a 2 inch (5 cm) tail; he looks silvery when swimming under water due to his fur holding a considerable quantity of air. This little fellow feeds on water gnats and whirligig beetles or routs on the bottom for caddis worms and other larvae; he loves exploring nooks and crannies but if he gets into a beer can he is unable to extricate himself.

All too often a minority group of anglers tend to give the fishing fraternity a bad name. Gossamer thin nylon fishing line lying around, often with one end securely caught in the branch of a tree, can prove a painful trap for an unsuspecting bird; it is not unknown for human limbs to suffer too from this menace.

Then of course there is the perennial problem of supermarket trolleys; recently when working on the river bank of a well known town I counted 80 trolleys showing above water in a relatively small area adjacent to a car park; in addition there were many more trolleys completely submerged. Perhaps we should put the clock back 1091 years, for at that time the water commissioner for the City of Rome, Sextus Julius Frontinus, ordered that a heavy fine be imposed upon any citizen found guilty of throwing rubbish into any river or watercourse.

5

Islands

The Thames and Shannon are the two rivers in the British Isles that are blessed with a great number of islands; on the Thames these are known as 'aits' or 'eyots', both words being pronounced 'eights'. Up until the middle of the nineteenth century a vast number of these aits were used as osier beds; in the past the growing of willows was an important and remunerative industry. Nowadays many of these islands are left in a natural state, so forming glorious havens for wildlife; some are used for recreational purposes, a few have boatyards or boat clubs upon them, others are used either for camping or summer residences, whilst a limited number have permanent dwellings built upon them. Some of the residences mentioned above owe a planning-free ancestry to the fact that they were developed from willow producers' seasonal headquarters, established by ancient right.

Many of our Thames aits are suffering badly from the effects of erosion; remedial work is urgently needed, as the Thames Heritage Trust is only too well aware. Some years ago the former Royal Borough of Windsor sought advice and re-instated Firework Ait, situated a little upstream of Windsor Bridge. The head of the ait was almost non-existent, the line was agreed with the Thames Conservancy (predecessors of the present Thames Water Authority) so that this part, which takes the full force of floodwater, was campshedded with interlocking steel sheets driven with a low freeboard (that is with only a short distance between normal water level and the top of the steel sheets). The rest of the island was stabilized with mattress type Maccaferri gabions suitably filled with graded material. These gabions, being woven, soon conform to the slope of the banks and the undulations of the ground. This type of gabion consists of a number of transverse pockets, with the unit being laid at right angles to the bank so that if and when erosion takes place, the end of the gabion curls downwards and acts as a self-sealing medium for preventing further under-cutting. The island had become almost barren; it was replanted with well chosen specimens and has for a very long time been well wooded with not only a natural look but a fine habitat for wildlife with easy access for waterfowl of all types.

With the re-organization of local authorities Windsor and Maidenhead councils united, and under this new authority two islands downstream of Boulter's lock on the Thames were restored. This necessitated

Firework Ait, Windsor: this was restored in the.early 1970s, great care being taken in both design and construction to ensure that results would be pleasing to the eye and beneficial for wildlife and herbage. On completion of restoration, the island was entirely barren and therefore has been entirely replanted.

Bridge Ait, Maidenhead, showing the hard line of steel piling which is neither aesthetically pleasing nor in sympathy with conservation interests.

protection of the banks; however, whilst this work was carried out to very high structural standards, sadly aesthetic values were overlooked. The work was carried out with high freeboard steel piling (which soon became rusty) and the resulting effect is that the islands look gaunt and unnatural especially as there is no hospitality for waterside plants: wildlife, unless airborne, can only gain access by using the lowered section of bank at the island's tail. Lack of thought of conservation and landscaping is all too apparent.

The time has come to take concerted action if we are to retain these magnificent features of the Thames – its islands.

Where there are eyots, it follows that there are backwaters. Some are fully navigable, others are only suitable for small craft, whilst a very few are extremely narrow and lush, with growth providing a haven for wildlife: one such little backwater I have in mind has salmon in its waters with the kingfisher nesting every year on the far steep bank. Dragonflies and damsel flies along with butterflies abound. Loosestrife, meadow-sweet and skullcap are in profusion with lady's smock growing on the adjoining grassy slope; down in the water is a lovely clump of waterlilies *(Nymphaea alba)*, which, along with the yellow brandy bottles *(Nuphar lutea)*, are becoming scarce due to their preference for still water. It is remote corners such as this that must be conserved and if possible re-created. Another narrow backwater I know had been silting up before it was dredged with loving care, to which nature responded with an increase in wildlife. That was a couple of years ago; now I am very sad to report that a landowner on the mainland bank has carried out some campshedding which is not only ugly but stands so high out of the water that it obscures the growth that was once clothing the bank. Water authority permission for such work should include other aspects, such as aesthetics, not purely land drainage.

A conference was held by the Conservators of the River Thames at Middlesex Guildhall on February 28th, 1947, to consider the whole question of the future of the Thames towpaths under the Conservators' jurisdiction, including their maintenance and upkeep, to which 37 riparian local and other authorities were invited. The conservators explained the position, not only from the point of view of the Thames navigation, but also concerning a right of way for the public to obtain access along the banks of the river. The conference appointed a committee to investigate the possibility of establishing a river walk along the towpath between Teddington and Cricklade.

Back in December 1949, The National Parks and Access to the Countryside Bill became an Act. The National Parks Commission was set up and designated three areas as National Parkland – Snowdonia, the Lakes and Peak District. In the same year (1949) a scheme was suggested for the Norfolk Broads as a National Park. This was followed in the summer of 1950 by a scheme put forward by architect and Thames man, Eric de Maré, to make the Thames a Linear National Park which would revive the idea of a continuous riverside walk as envisaged by the Thames River Preservation Committee in 1884, which in turn was based upon an idea promulgated in 1793. The whole concept of a riverside walk covering the 135 miles of riverbank from Lechlade to Teddington received much impetus from the former Thames Conservancy and at a meeting of the Thames River Walk Committee in March 1956 the idea was unanimously approved by representatives of all the riparian authorities interested.

In 1980 there was further momentum when the Thames Water Authority came to a formal decision to give its 'general principle to the concept of a continuous Thames Walk'.

In 1988, after much hard work, meetings and consultations, this wonderful scheme was extended to 156 miles; running from the source to Putney, the walk will, by the time this book is published, be almost finished, another jewel in the crown for the Countryside Commission.

The Thames Heritage Trust was formed as a charity in 1980 on the inspiration of John Coleman, O.B.E. It was to encourage a better appreciation of the importance of preserving the Thames and its environment as a national heritage. In practical terms this involves instituting projects relating to the improvement of banks and riverside walks. Looking after the river and its banks is not a statutory obligation of any one body, although many organizations play their parts, some public, some private and some voluntary. With such diverse interests, it is inevitable that there are grey areas of responsibility. It is these areas that the Trust aims to cover.

Since its formation the Trust has been carrying out much needed towpath repair work, mainly in conjunction with the Manpower Services Commission and with financial help from Thames Water, appropriate local authorities and very welcome donations.

Thames towpaths owe their origin to the general introduction of horse towing in the latter part of the eighteenth century. Of late, there has been criticism from some quarters regarding the width of restored and repaired towpaths. To clarify the situation it must be stated that when towpaths were made, the generally accepted width of them was that which gave a single horse room to turn round and face the opposite direction. Furthermore, in towing an 80-ton barge upstream under winter conditions there could have been as many as 14 massive Shire horses breasted up as a single team.

6

Wildlife

The rivers and waterways of Britain are one of the main components of our great landscape, which is renowned for its beauty throughout the world. However the landscape is invariably in a state of change: the ever-growing demand for improved drainage, nowadays carried out by mechanical means, threatens the character of our landscape to the extent that many features such as delightful little side streams, trees – from mighty specimens to fascinating clumps of alder – waterside plants and moisture-loving herbage are affected and in many cases disappear completely.

It is generally accepted that there is a very real need for conservation upon the rivers and canals of this country; unfortunately the word 'conservation' is so often bandied around as if it were some panacea producing quick results; it is no substitute for the fine old practice of good husbandry which is a combination of a philosophical outlook, very good forward management ability and an inherent understanding of nature, all tempered with patience, and not forgetting the fact that rivers in particular are chuckling, living entities with a will of their own.

River management can be split into two sections: (a) maintenance works and (b) major alterations, generally referred to as 'river improvement schemes', which in the main are for the alleviation of flooding, also drainage improvement. The latter involves dredging to deepen the river, straightening of the banks to lessen sharp bends and/or the making of by-pass channels, smoothing the bed and on occasion creating steep embankments to contain floodwater. All this is in the interests of removing excess water with utmost speed from troublesome areas.

However, as a result of such works, pools, meanders and shallows, which are essential for some fish, are replaced by a graded bed; the banks may lose their shallow edges which are so important for the marginal growth of such plants as kingcups, water forget-me-not, yellow flag, purple loosestrife, watermint and meadow-sweet. Any such loss of flora has, needless to say, a knock-on effect in that there is no habitat for wildlife. Then, as if to add insult to injury, the time comes when river improvement schemes necessitate the removal of trees and thick growth, which in their own right often hold a bank together with their fibrous roots. Their canopy gives shelter and food

for many species of birds, besides providing shade; the resulting increase of light penetrating the shallow water and spreading across the bank enables plants such as sweet grass, fool's watercress and bur-reed to grow, to the detriment of the other plants.

Trees also (as mentioned in an earlier chapter) do much to alleviate summer flooding. The gnarled semi-undermined roots of alder and other trees provide the ideal day-time resting-up place for otters and other creatures. Daubenton's bat is such an expert at catching insects close to the surface of the water that it is sometimes referred to as 'the water bat'. In winter these bats hibernate in old buildings, caves and canal tunnels but enjoy the shelter of the hollow of a willow or similar tree in the summer.

The lives and habits of birds and animals provide never-ending fascination and pleasure. The greatest satisfaction that can be obtained is sharing our waterways with these many and varied inhabitants as opposed to watching them from afar with binoculars. I find the relaxed way of uniting with wildlife and observing the activities of birds and animals is to sleep in the open beneath the stars, or clouds, as the weather dictates. An essential item is a really good quality sleeping bag, which incidentally should be of a colour to merge with the surroundings. In late evening and into the night, then again from

A selection of waterside inhabitants.

first light onwards, the activities and happenings along the bank can be captivating.

I mentioned the water shrew in another chapter, but a further favourite of mine is the water vole, often insulted by being called a water rat; there is no such animal as a water rat, it is purely the folk name given to the water vole, which is neither a rat nor of a rat-like nature. The water vole is quite heavily built with a short thickish head and appealing rounded face; when swimming, his body is about two-thirds submerged and from a distance looks like a large twig on the surface. Its main food is bankside herbage, also river bed grubs. As these creatures do not hibernate, they invariably lay up a store of food so as to be prepared for a hard winter. The water vole is a clean and inoffensive animal; when burrowing he can, however, cause serious damage when the bank is of a canal or artificial watercourse that is above surrounding ground; if the little burrow so formed causes a leak, it can in some circumstances turn into a breach. At breeding time the female, with the help of her mate, makes a beautiful moss lined nest in which to rear her young – usually about five to a litter.

Water vole with nest.

Like their fellow mammals, otters and shrews, voles enjoy plenty of vegetation, for this offers not only food but cover from predators, man included. Apart from digging their main burrow, storage and nursery burrows, they also like to have feeding burrows in close proximity to their foraging grounds in order to take cover quickly should an emergency arise. As these burrows are at, or near, water level, it can be appreciated that campshedding is not conducive to the happy or productive life of the water vole.

It is generally recognized that in a very high wind pollarded trees are the safest; in the great gale of October 1987, I observed a squirrel had built a drey well up in a 70-foot high tree where she had a late litter; just 6 days before the storm she hurriedly made another drey in the crown of a pollarded tree about 40 yards away and then moved her kittens, one at a time, by carrying them in her mouth to the new drey. From this it would seem that nature was in advance of both the barometer and the meteorologists. Squirrels are adept at swimming and I have known more than one island to be populated with them.

When lying motionless in the sleeping bag, it has given me great pleasure to watch a kingfisher at very close quarters, fishing and enjoying his resultant breakfast. Another fascinating bird is the heron who usually fishes in shallow waters; he takes up his position on the adjacent bank or foreshore where he stands motionless until an unsuspecting fish swims past. At that point the heron shoots his head forward and with perfect aim captures the fish, crushes it to death and then swallows it head first. Should the heron be fishing deeper waters he still stands motionless with his large wings neatly folded – like an old gentleman in coat tails. The folded wings trap air which enable him to bob to the surface like a cork out of a bottle after catching his prey. Herons nest in the tops of trees; they like company, so keep together, thus forming

HERON

GREAT CRESTED GREBE

LITTLE GREBE

COOT

heronries. They come to the same trees year after year and invariably use the same nests after a little tidying and making good. Over a very long period of time the trees die from over-population, but last year a big heronry near me was nigh on wiped out as a result of the great gale of October 1987. However, several pairs returned early in 1988 and with the subsequent surge of growth it looks as though the old heronry will be re-colonized.

The coot is a cautious bird and, although an excellent diver, it lives on land as much as water. Although the coot is often regarded as a bit stupid, his looks and actions are misleading for he is quite capable of flying long distances, a point proved by ringing, when English coots have been found in Europe and Scandinavia. Little grebes, otherwise known as 'dabchicks', are fascinating divers that pop down to the depths at the rate of ten times a minute to catch small fry, larvae and fresh-water shrimps. The great crested grebe is also a very good diver, a handsome bird, once scarce due to being caught for its feathers, which were in demand by milliners. However, numbers are now increasing rapidly.

Canada geese are in abundance, so much so that they can pose a problem for farmers inasmuch that a single goose can eat more grass in a day than a sheep. I noticed that it was after the great freeze-up of 1963 that these birds started multiplying at an unprecedented rate on the Thames. Geese can however play a very useful role in feeding on, and clearing, very weedy waters.

Swans are graceful birds which pair for life and have been very much in the news the last few years due to their recent habit of swallowing lead shot which often leads to their premature death. As a result of the harmful effects of lead upon these birds there are now quite a number of voluntary organizations running 'swan hospitals' and swan rescue services. Possibly the largest such service is the one based at Shotesham St Mary near Norwich; however lead poisoning is only one of many problems they suffer which include being entangled in fishing gear, abused by hooligans, gummed up with oil and 'downed' by power cables. If a swan has to be pushed away from a potential danger, or is getting too close to small children it will soon glide away if splashed with water. There are areas where swans (and other waterfowl) are sickened with kindness by being fed with far too much bread and starch related products; often they are so well fed that they cease hunting and so their natural instincts are curtailed.

On canals and slow flowing rivers conditions are ideal for dragon-flies; the Emperor is a British species and a real beauty whilst the blue tailed damselfly is a species that can be found on waterways in built-up areas.

Otters, or the scarcity of them, have led to a lot of interest. In various areas they are on the increase and the sight of baby otters playing is a wonderful experience; as with all youngsters they love a bit of fun and plenty of play. Their parents have to teach them to swim and make slides down the bank so that the little ones can enjoy slipping into the water at speed. The otter population has decreased, but with undefiled waters, an abundance of fish and a little help from man, together with freedom from disturbance and plenty of scrubby cover, there is no reason why we should not see a resurgence of these charming mammals. However it must be remembered that too much cleaning up of river banks and overdoing bank protection works is likely to move any possible otter population completely away.

This brings me to a point about re-stocking lakes and other waters with geese, ducks, swans and kindred birds; there are now wildfowl farms around who can supply such creatures, subject to availability. By the time this book is published we may find that the tiny marsh warbler is no longer returning to this country after its winter migration in East Africa. Ornithologists claim the demise of these dear fellows is due to modern farming and cleaning up of river valleys. One of their favourite breeding grounds was the Severn-Avon valleys; some were observed last season on the riverbank near Tewkesbury, but very few.

Riparian contractors in carrying out their work invariably show little or no thought for fish – is out of sight out of mind? Things to bear in mind are bankwork: wherever practicable leave some under-cuts, particularly beneath alder trees, for they provide fish shelters. On farmland banks, cattle should be kept back to prevent damage to banks with their hoofs with resultant loss of vegetation that can give, besides shelter for fish, a source of food in the form of grubs and so on dropping into the water. When dredging, leave some patches of weed and submerged and emergent plants, for they are often feeding and breeding grounds. Maintain as many overhanging trees as possible, along with overhanging vegetation for insects falling from this growth are tasty fish food.

Fish do like shelter from the fastest currents; an obstruction such as a tree trunk or large log is often appreciated, even by trout. Young fish enjoy shallow and/or weedy water where they feel secure from the greedy clutches of a pike. In the same way that riparian work, as already mentioned, should be carried out in conjunction with a landscape architect, so when it comes to a fishing river, it is wise for a contractor carrying out specific work to discuss the operation with the area fishery officer.

Another once popular item for the table were crayfish. On the Thames the crayfish population was virtually wiped out by disease towards the end of the nineteenth century; although it has not recovered, many other rivers – the Kennet included – are well endowed with crayfish; furthermore I understand that supplies for stocking streams and rivers are now available from specialist fish farms.

Fear not, all is not doom and gloom! The Surrey and Hampshire Canal Society is doing fine work on the Basingstoke Canal. There is a great interest in bat colonies in the Greywell tunnel through which the old canal used to pass in order to reach the town of Basingstoke. The difference of opinion between those wishing to retain the colonies and those wanting to restore the navigation is seemingly being resolved. Greywell tunnel is now scheduled by the Nature Conservancy Council as a Site of Special Scientific Interest (S.S.S.I.), like other sites, such as Port Meadow at Oxford. The boatyard at Port Meadow, although within an S.S.S.I., appears to work in harmony with the N.C.C. (Nature Conservancy Council). Lampreys, of olden times considered a delicacy, seem to be a thing of the past; possibly dredging and modern river management has reduced the muddy living areas of this primitive fishlike vertebrate.

The management of British Waterways has made great strides in the re-establishment of canal flora, which in turn makes hunting the nesting areas for wildlife. Way back in the early 1960s the British

The modern fish pass at Molesey.

Waterways Board were experimenting with methods of bank protection that would not inhibit the growth of plants and that would be environmentally pleasing. In this direction they tried out what was then a new product, 'Famliner', a material based on fibreglass which had a high bitumen content. All seemed well for a start but the following spring the emergent plants enjoyed the beneficial effects of bitumen upon root growth, so much that they grew at an unprecedented rate to the embarrassment of navigation! Remains of the experiment are still visible today at Kilworth on the Leicester section of the Grand Union Canal. It is heartening that the British Waterways Board gives conscientious attention to conservation, including landscaping and architecture.

Most of our river authorities are now taking a much more enlightened view and are providing various facilities such as salmon ladders on the Thames; these 'ladders' used to be a series of troughs arranged stepwise and with alternate changes in the position of the side openings near the ends, so that water flows gently down in a zig-zag stream against which the salmon easily make their way. However, modern 'ladders' or 'passes' are the sophisticated result of modern research and technology.

The Thames was first in the field in appointing a conservation officer, which excellent idea was soon followed by other water authorities. Another move by Thames Water was the use of geotextiles (Nicospan) on land drainage work, the success of which has spread to their use of it on the main river with a view to maintaining natural-looking banks.

The South West Water Authority has excelled itself on more than one occasion: this year (1988), after a survey in conjunction with the Royal Society for the Protection of Birds, arrangements were made for no work to be carried out on riverbanks frequented by sand martins

A cross-section giving an idea for an artificial otter holt.

from the time of their arrival in March until their return to Africa in the autumn, so as to give these now scarce visitors a chance to nest. The reason for their scarcity, in common with warblers, fly catchers and other birds of Southern Africa, is that they have suffered great losses resulting from a succession of droughts in their African winter quarters as well as further drought areas situated on their migratory route to England. Martins, like kingfishers, excavate their nests in riverbanks, safely away from stoats and weasels.

Several years ago, South West Water created some artificial otter holts. These can be made with logs, boulders, walling stone or any such natural material that is close to hand; the general shape is roughly circular with a diameter of about 3 feet to 3 feet 6 inches (1 to 1 ¼ metres), whilst two entrance/exit tunnels must be provided; the top can be of logs, stone slabs or timbers covered with soil, river gravel, turf or bankside debris to blend with surroundings. Secluded positions must be chosen for these structures, away from human eyes and any possible disturbance. If bankside trees need cutting or coppicing on a river that is known to be visited by otters, then a check should be made to see if any are used as holts; if so, they should be clearly marked to ensure that they are not cut down. Also sufficient saplings must be left to grow into trees for continuity of holt sites. I have had pleasure in watching these lovely creatures on various occasions and often in unusual situations; when writing my book *The Thames from source to tideway* in 1981 I expressed the opinion that '... it is quite possible that they [otters] are getting used to boats and civilization in the same way as the fox is accepting urban surroundings'. Now seven years later I have information on an otter building a holt in an old garden shed, in a relatively well populated area, and raising a litter of cubs. The otter's nesting holt is lined by the bitch with reeds, grass and moss, but also included are twigs; these are not for snugness but rather to ensure air flow through the nesting material which in turn helps to keep it dry.

7

Conservation of Structures

On the building side there is also need for conservation; a very important item on many waterways is the retention of remaining public wharves and their maintenance in good usable order. Those that are run down require attention in the form of dredging to ensure good access and structural repairs as required. All too often the approach to wharves is silted up, or the local authority has turned the area into a public garden.

There are numerous items to be seen along our rivers and canals that add charm and character, particularly in urban areas. Objects that spring to mind are some of the lovely old hand-operated cranes of a by-gone age and the variety of well worn mooring bollards, both of timber and cast iron. Bridges too have a special place, particularly those lovely little lifting ones on the Llangollen and Oxford canals which are probably equal in fascination to many of the old cast-iron bridges, particularly those split ones on the Staffordshire and Worcestershire Canal that allow a tow rope to pass between the two cantilevered projections of the bridge. Other architectural and engineering items of great interest are both aqueducts and tunnels, normally well cared

Cast-iron bridge carrying the Oxford Canal towpath across the River Cherwell where it joins the canal.

Lifting bridge on the Oxford Canal.

for by the British Waterways Board.

It gives me pleasure to say that the British Waterways Board are very conscious of such delights and do their utmost to maintain high standards; for example, when Stoke Bruerne Bridge required strengthening work (which was virtually a rebuild), they ensured that their contractors faced it with period style bricks, so, when completed, the waterway traveller was unaware of a major reconstruction having taken place.

Old warehouses, often of timber, invariably had a projection over the water from the upper floor so that sacks of grain, flour or general merchandise could be lifted directly from the hold of a narrow boat or barge under dry conditions. A good example of this style of warehouse

Lifting bridge on the Welsh section of the Shropshire Union Canal.

exists at Aynho on the Oxford Canal.

Whilst preserving items of the past is almost a cult these days, it should not prevent us from ensuring that mundane items such as picnic tables, benches and rubbish bins are well designed and well made. Incidentally, in many areas, these need to be both squirrel- and fox-proof. I know riverside areas where foxes have, in the fishing season, scattered bin contents far and wide with the consequence that anglers have been roundly chastised.

Mooring rings and bollards are essential on any navigable waterway; the production of a range of cast iron bollards is steadily being increased to cover the styles of the various regions, for example the Grand Junction Canal, Regent's Canal, Trent and Mersey Canal and the Grand Union. The latest introduction is a cast-iron disabled symbol that can be fitted to the above bollards when used on moorings for the disabled; plans are afoot to develop and increase this much needed facility.

With the advent of widespread pleasure boating in the relatively early part of the nineteenth century the construction of boathouses upon private riverside properties commenced and grew steadily until the coming of the steam launch, when larger boathouses were needed. The usual 'tell tale' for a steam launch building is a louvred 'pigeon box' straddling the ridge of the roof and positioned lengthwise so that it would be directly over the vessel's funnel; this enabled the smoke and smuts to escape into the atmosphere, which must have made life more pleasant for the party that was about to go afloat. The peak of boathouse building was around the turn of the century; types varied but most were 'wet', that is, the boathouse itself was built over a wet dock excavated out of the bank at right angles to the river. A 'dry' boathouse was a building constructed over a concrete or brick floor ramped down to the water's edge. Many boathouses had an upper storey used as a summerhouse in season and as flood free storage space for boat gear during the winter: some were, and for that matter still are, real rivermen's dens with faded sepia photographs of club groups and events, regatta trophies and sundry sculls and blades from a by-gone era.

Dry boathouses built for the protection of punts, skiffs and gigs, if situated in an area liable to serious flooding, had no side cladding between the floor and the base of the room above, but instead had slatting so that flood water would not be impeded. It was customary with the coming of winter to hoist the boats and hold them in slings from the beams above. The slatted sides referred to were often known as 'modesty screens' so that men could change into their swimming costumes without embarrassment to the ladies.

A large number of boathouses of all types still exist; some have been extensively restored, a few have been very well maintained over the years, quite a lot are beyond redemption, whilst there is a goodly number that with a little loving care could be brought back into use. With the resurgence in the use of skiffs, dinghies and punts many of the smaller boathouses could once again prove valuable assets. The roofing of boathouses was very often carried out with clay tiles and in the Victorian era invariably finished off with decorative ridge tiles culminating in a terracotta embellishment or finial; some were prize pieces by such famous artists as George Tinworth of Doulton's whilst others were from artists and potteries long since forgotten, but nevertheless still very delightful.

Watermills always hold great fascination and many of these have been renovated to a very high standard, so much so that some not only have their machinery in working order but are even producing stone ground flour, as for example Mapledurham; whilst others although outwardly looking as of yore have in fact been gutted of all machinery. In some cases where the building has been converted for other uses, at least the external appearance has been maintained, and more often than not is cared for in an exemplary manner.

Waterwheels were used for providing power for many purposes; an interesting example is down in Sussex on the River Rother, alongside Coultershaw Bridge, where a waterwheel and bean pump were built and installed in 1790 for the purpose of pumping water to the small town of Petworth some 1 ½ miles away; the pipe carrying the water was of 3 inch bore and at some time after the initial installation an air vessel was incorporated in the delivery pipe to reduce pressure fluctuations. The pump was in use until about 1960 delivering an estimated 20,000 gallons per day: it then fell into disuse, but in 1976 restoration of the machinery was commenced by the Sussex Industrial

Hard landscaping with landing stages and cast-iron bollards at Swan's Reach residential development, Harefield, Grand Union Canal.

Archaeology Society and now the whole outfit is in first class condition and can be viewed on specified 'open' days.

The very thought, or rumour, of marina construction, let alone waterside residential development, is a sure way of raising the hackles of local inhabitants. But, looking at any such situation objectively, it must be borne in mind that by nature we are all somewhat conservative; as creatures of habit, we are inclined to abhor sudden change, and the human trait of selfishness can surreptitiously creep in. The thought of a marina being developed in one's favourite reach of river or idyllic canal site can be horrific. However, our waterways are here for all to enjoy and that new marina could be paradise for boatowners living in a crowded town that is but a reasonable motor journey away.

Property developers have at long last realized the great potential of building residences in the form of houses, flats or maisonettes alongside rivers and canals or excavating areas for marinas with residential development on the perimeter. There was a time in the 1960s when developers were anxious to advertise properties as having moorings, but were reluctant to spend money on the necessary work. Thank goodness the situation has changed dramatically and today they are not only anxious to provide first-class mooring facilities but to make them as environmentally pleasing as possible. Moorings of course increase the value of property, but for a long time developers fought shy of the extra cost until they found that sales increased and values appreciated.

In the early days of marinas and moorings the majority of camping boats and cruisers were in the 16 to 23 feet class and when purpose-built narrow boats for cruising appeared on the scene they were around 30 to 35 feet long, against the traditional working boats of 72 feet. Since those days the private narrow boats have been increased in length and at the time of writing it looks as though the 50-footer is going to be *de rigueur*. The same applies to river cruisers.

Many marinas are now self-contained, even running a club with clubhouse and all facilities: with some large residential waterside sites 'estate' clubs are in existence or being formed. Waterside public houses and hotels have always had good car parking facilities but it is only in recent times, with a few exceptions, that they have really put their mind to the desirability of good moorings. At one time it was hard work convincing publicans and brewers that not only would it be in the public interest, but a great help to their trade to have sound moorings for visiting boats. After installation of proper facilities, I have heard, more than once, from publicans, 'I wish I had done this before.' Furthermore, well designed and carefully created moorings can greatly enhance the waterside of most hotels and pubs. We have now almost gone full circle from the days when hostelries obtained good trade from waterborne traffic and provided stabling for horses engaged in towing narrow boats and barges. When local towns complain that they do not get extra trade from holidaymakers afloat, the answer is usually that their mooring facilities are either non-existent or inadequate.

Jetties, sometimes referred to as landing stages, are structures that can be built to harmonize with the environment. The latest type, developed by a riparian specialist firm in conjunction with a very progressive timber company, uses wooden piles and stringers (the longitudinal members) that have been machine turned, so making them perfectly round. The deck boards are of half round timber which are secured into scollops, ready machined along the tops of the stringers at appropriate centres. All the timber is pressure treated to the British Standards Specification, giving a life of 40 years. There is a further specification covering treatment of timber that is in permanent or intermittent contact with water.

The most popular solution used in pressure treating leaves the wood with a greenish-grey colour which blends well with nature; there are shades of brown and also at extra cost a rich copper colour. Should you belong to the 'natural finish brigade', i.e. timber as sawn, then a clear solution can be used. For timber works generally, whether landing stage, capping for steel campshedding or other woodwork, an architectural range of colour preservatives is available for cosmetic application after the timber has undergone its pressure preservative treatment.

A point to remember is that pressure-treated timber will, according to weather conditions, show hairline cracks and slight movement; however this is no cause for concern. Some hardwoods have been known to reject preservatives. When using timber treated to the basic B.S.S. (giving a life of 20 years) I have found it advantageous to give an annual brush coat of preservative, especially if the woodwork concerned is facing the sun.

8

Riverside Planting

There are some conservationists who may be termed 'purists' who are insistent that everything planted or sown is a species native to this country: whilst that is an admirable sentiment, I have met some enthusiasts adamant on this point who fail to realize that some of the trees and plants which they regard as native were actually brought into this country many years ago. The answer is that one must be realistic about the situation and also differentiate between the planting up of the wild or natural bank and the landscaping of a riparian estate, private garden, camping plot or modern development.

Choice of trees is important and one of the favourite for all forms of waterside planting is the willow. This well known tree genus is as old as any of the earliest recorded plants; in origin it is pre-ice age with virtually a world-wide distribution. Left in its wild state, without as much as a helping hand from man, it is amongst the first vegetation to appear on land that has been devastated by fire, earthquake or other traumatic events. The botanical name for willow – *Salix* – is generally understood to be derived from the Celtic *Sal* = 'near' and *Lis* = 'water'. An interesting feature of willows is the presence of a bitter white substance in the bark known as salicin from which is obtained acetyl-salicyllic acid used in pain killing tablets; hence it is not surprising to find elderly arthritic-bound animals nibbling the bark of willow trees. Another use of willow bark is for tanning, it being preferable to oak for Russian leather.

World-wide there are some 200 species of willow, about 10% of these being native to the British Isles, whilst many have hybridized among themselves so giving variations with attendant problems and confusion over nomenclature. There are some willows that are grown for commercial purposes to which reference will be made in due course; otherwise choice depends on requirement such as growth, ultimate height, colour of wood in winter, catkins in spring and similar factors.

Different parts of the willow were used by man and each had its own name; a 'withy' is the thin whippy growth removed from willows for the making of ties – so pre-dating the use of string; the word 'osier' is derived from the Latin *'ausaria'* which literally means a willow bed. Varieties of willow such as *Salix viminalis* and *salix purpurea* are very suitable for producing rods for basket-making;

Withy cutting (on left) *and willow pollarding.*

in the passage of time trees coppiced for rods for basket-making (i.e. cut down to the ground and allowed to shoot again) tended to be referred to as 'osiers' as opposed to pollarded willows, often referred to quite simply as 'pollards'.

Willow provides excellent timber for farms and estates for such items as fencing, gate-hurdles, ladders, hay rakes and numerous other items as diverse as paddles for water mills and gunstocks. To produce the correct type of wood, trees are pollarded, that is the crown is cut off so that many young branches are thrown up in a tight cluster: when grown to the required size they are removed in winter time, allowing fresh breaks to appear the following spring to produce a further crop for cutting in five to six years' time. Popular varieties for producing 'poles' are *Salix vitellina, Salix alba* and *Salix chrysostella*; the new wood of the last named is a fine red and looks magnificent in winter time. *Salix coerulea* (the bat willow) is grown for producing cricket bats; it is not pollarded but grown as a standard tree. When young, side shoots are rubbed out in order to produce a straight knot-free trunk, which can reach maturity in twenty years.

A fairly new variety of willow, *Salix aqua gigantea*, has been bred to provide timber for Scandinavian style wood-burning stoves: it can be cropped every third year by cutting the convenient sized stems at ground level. Sometimes it proves a useful crop for that parcel of ground that becomes too moist for other uses. I have written more about willows than I first intended but I think there is still good potential for growing and cropping willows on suitable waterside sites. Many farmers are now diversifying their activities, and there is a resurgence in willow-derived products for home, garden and general use, from furniture, fencing panels and rose arches to lobster pots and eel traps, to name but a few examples.

In concluding, I would end as I started, with a note on native species of willow. The weeping willow, *Salix babylonica*, is universally accepted for its beauty; but though many people believe it to be native of this country or the Holy Lands, it is in fact a native of China. It was named by the great botanist Linnaeus who mistakenly thought a willow of such beauty could only come from beside the waters of Babylon. In the days when the Chinese exported ginger to Europe, they used the very thin and flexible 'withies' from this tree for tying and securing the small parcels of ginger. It was from one of these withies that a cutting was made and struck so forming the parent of all 'our' babylonicas. According to records the first babylonica grown in this country was planted beside the Thames at Twickenham in 1730.

A prolific and homely native waterside tree is the common alder, *Alnus glutinosa*. It enjoys damp situations unsuited to other trees and will grow to a height of 50 to 90 feet (15 to 27 metres) with a trunk girth of up to 12 feet (3 ½ metres). It is of a pyramidal habit; its bright red fibrous roots are excellent for stabilizing riverbanks; when the main roots on a mature tree become undermined or minor erosion takes place the resultant cavities form popular resting places for otters, as already mentioned. This is a tree for planting on natural or undeveloped banks and is definitely one not to be planted alongside boat moorings, for the catkins which appear in February later shed their contents to leave a brown stain on the boats below; this menace is even worse when the weather is wet. The timber of this tree was used some decades back in Lancashire for the manufacture of clogs; there was a time at the beginning of the century when the demand for clogs exceeded the supply of alder, and birch was substituted. There are many varieties of alder emanating from Europe and North America; one such type, *Alnus incana*, is often found, commonly called the grey alder: it was introduced into this country in 1780. A most accommodating tree is the native silver birch, *Betula alba*: birches have, like willows, been growing in the British Isles for somewhere between 18,000 and 20,000 years! A delightful variety is Young's weeping birch *Betula alba pendula youngi*, a most elegant tree and suitable for small gardens and confined spaces.

Betula nigra is the river birch, a native of the United States

CORKSCREW WILLOW

ASPEN

TAXODIUM

METASEQUOIA   HEMLOCK FIR

introduced to this country in 1736. It forms a fine pyramidal tree 50 to 90 feet (15 to 27 metres) high, often forked low down which with its curling bark gives it a picturesque ruggedness.

An American resident in this country since 1750 is *Betula papyrifera*, the paper birch, which can grow to a magnificent 70 foot (21 metre) high specimen and in the garden can be used to great effect, thanks to its brilliant white bark. This is the birch used for making canoes, drinking troughs and roofing buildings.

Poplars form a large group of quick-growing trees which are related to the willow family and occur in most parts of the northern hemisphere; some grow in arid places whilst others delight in moist situations. *Populus balsamifera* is a rapid grower and can end up as a 100 foot (30 metre) giant. The very great joy of this tree is the fragrance of balsam which pervades the evening air in spring and early summer. Other good varieties are the grey poplar, *Populus canescens*, and *nigra*, the black poplar; both of these grow to a height of around 100 feet

(30 metres). *Populus tremula*, the aspen, only grows to about 50 feet (15 metres): an attribute of the aspen is the perpetual quivering of the leaves, 'to tremble like an aspen leaf' being a phrase which goes back to Spenser's time.

When carrying out planting schemes the choice is considerable for natural and wild sites, whilst in private gardens and riparian parkland the choice is virtually limitless: for example, there are those two tremendous and very handsome deciduous conifers, the water fir *(Metasequoia glyptostroboides)* and the swamp cypress *(Taxodium distichum)*. Both of these trees have foliage that is dainty and fern-like with a delightful green hue which is very bright in spring: before the leaves fall in autumn the foliage changes to a rusty pink.

The *Taxodium* is a pyramidal tree growing to a height of 100 to 150 feet (30 to 45 metres) and hails from the southern area of the United States; it arrived in this country early in the seventeenth century. In very damp situations the roots produce quaint woody protuberances which stand up out of the ground: these enable the root system to breathe when the tree is growing in a really wet situation; on the other hand *Taxodium* will grow well under normal garden conditions.

The water fir, although visually similar in many respects, is outstanding, inasmuch that it is a relatively new introduction having been discovered by the Chinese in north-east Szechwan, where it grows in river valleys and on swampy ground, as recently as 1945. It can attain a height of around 100 feet (30 metres); in this country it has grown to a height of 16 feet (5 metres) in six years from seed.

Tsuga or hemlock fir spruces really enjoy waterside sites, providing drainage is good. Most species of this genus make large trees of great charm. *Tsuga canadensis*, the western hemlock, has a variety 'Pendula' which makes a comparatively small tree forming an umbrella of dense foliage.

Where a tree of restricted height is required, say about 25 to 30 feet (7 to 9 metres), then *Rhus typhina*, the stag's horn sumach, so well known for its scarlet foliage in autumn, has much to recommend it.

Shrubs have an important part to play; bushy growth along a riverbank gives cover for wildlife including some of the lovely butterflies and interesting moths, and whilst on the subject of butterflies, I have noticed that the red admiral seems to have a great affinity for meadow-sweet, a plant that grows so well at the water's edge.

The roots of shrubs also help with bank stabilization and if a towpath is being used for its intended purpose, then there is usually room for a tow rope to perform its duty without any encumbrance. I will not make a catalogue of shrubs but would mention that many people do not seem to be aware of the many shrubby willows that are available, such as *Salix phylicifolia*, the tea leaf willow; *Salix rosmarinifolia*, which looks much like the old fashioned herb, rosemary, is often called hoary willow due to its greyish leaves. Furthermore, there is a distinct group of willows consisting of large bushy shrubs and small trees referred to as Sallows. Amongst them is *Salix caprea*, the goat willow (synonymous with 'the great sallow'), where large yellow male catkins are known as 'palm', whilst the female form with silver catkins is called 'pussy willow'. The white wood of this tree makes first-class charcoal and products such as tannin and salicin are taken from it. A willow that does not grow into a large tree is *Salix matsudana tortuosa*, the Hankow corkscrew tree; as it grows its branches spiral upwards in a clockwise fashion, which in winter give a charming silhouette, fit for a Chinese painting.

Salix aquatica is the water sallow and, as its name implies, it flourishes in very wet places. It grows into a large bush but rarely forms a tree.

Mention of charcoal brings us round to *Cornus* – the extensive family of dogwoods whose red stems in winter always bring welcome cheery colour to the scene. The wood of these shrubs makes good charcoal and I am informed by an expert that *Cornus alba elegantissima* – the variegated dogwood – is much sought after in the manufacture of gunpowder.

Having thrown out suggestions with regard to specimens for the waterside, I feel a few words about planting and after care would not be amiss.

Whether preparing a scheme, or actually carrying out the planting, it is most important to visualize what the tree or shrub in question will be like when fully grown. Often trees, and sometimes shrubs, are planted too close together and on some development sites forest type trees are planted in too great a proximity to buildings which is neither practical nor aesthetically pleasing. Good soil is essential for healthy growth and, if anything has to be added, then well rotted leaf mould is the ideal medium and I find preferable to many of the proprietary composts that are available. When planting, ensure that the roots are making good contact with the soil (usually done by shaking the tree in a vertical position as the loam is being run into the opening). This loose loam must be well firmed, which must be done with the heel of your boot – never the sole. Firmness of planting is the key to success.

Staking is advisable, not so much to prevent stems from fracturing but to curtail tree movement until the young tree has made its own roots into the surrounding ground, by which time it is well anchored. Trees, like everything else, have to be cared for, which means that damaged or unwanted growth must be removed and furthermore a good tree surgeon will keep a fine tree well balanced so rendering it less likely to become the victim of any violent gale. Tree surgery is very skilled work, often handed down from father to son or else learned by hard won experience. The British Standards Institution has standards laid down not only for arboricultural practice but also for landscape work and even specifications for willows and poplars for timber production. Remember that the other end of the tree, namely the roots, requires attention under certain conditions. Trees growing naturally on the riverbank, hedgerow, copse or wood have the benefit of the leaves falling to the ground around them during the autumn; these leaves decompose to provide nourishment and soil improvement for the trees in question. Trees growing in a private garden or public open space have a different set of conditions, for in such confines it is invariably general practice to clear up all the leaves as they fall; in most gardens they are put on a compost heap to be used, when rotted, for applying to the ground. Sadly local authorities are prone to incinerate their leaves. However they are dealt with, the trees then lack their natural annual feed; in consequence this should be made good by forking in well rotted leaf mould or compost or applying a balanced organic fertilizer.

A killer disease of trees if *Armillaria mellea*, otherwise known as honey fungus. This fungus spreads through the soil by means of rhizomorphs which grow at the rate of about a metre per year; upon coming into contact with the roots of living plants they are able to penetrate the tissues and grow beneath the inner layers of the bark. Mats of fungal growth develop, the fungus becomes parasitic on the plant tissues and so the root is eventually killed. If no living tree is available, *Armellaria* will attack dead wood; whilst various specifics are available, prevention is better than cure, so always collect prunings, etc, and burn them and avoid using logs for garden edging or slices of them for 'stepping stones'. If you do wish to use timber for this purpose buy material from the timber mill that has been pressure treated with preservative. Finally, after good hygiene, a very important item is good cultural conditions with special attention to *drainage* and *nutrition*. Honey fungus is the biggest killer of trees in the country; if you are in doubt about any specimen it is wise to contact your area Ministry of Agriculture office.

As I have said in an earlier chapter, when remedial work is carried out to a riverbank, landscaping and aesthetic practices are usually conspicuous by their absence. In many cases when campshedding is being done, contractors tend to remove trees at the water's edge rather than go to the trouble – often very tedious – of preserving them. Sometimes on a bank, just maintaining one single tree is sufficient to give balance and character, especially if it is a magnificent Huntingdon willow *(Salix alba)* or that truly regal weeping willow, *Salix salamonii* (which is a cross between *Salix alba* and *Salix babylonica*).

When planning a riverside garden, it must be borne in mind that the area of land in question is going to be part of a linear landscape and must be viewed as such. What would be quite acceptable on a residential estate or in suburban surroundings is not necessarily suitable for a riverbank. Therefore, designing a garden is not just a matter of hard graft at the drawing board, but also good knowledge of the growth that trees and shrubs will produce together with an artistic eye for shape and form; a fine garden is rather like a charming watercolour where the character is of greater concern than explicit detail.

Possibly we should pay more attention to emulating the Chinese, whose word for landscape is 'shan shui', which translated literally means hills and water, both of which are requisite components in the creation of a garden, for water induces tranquillity whilst hills provide stimulation. With a waterside garden height must be balanced by depth, the outline of a rugged rock relieved by soft vegetation and the play of light intensified by shadows. Contrast is of very great importance, but it must be a factor that is restrained and never obvious, in fact subtlety is the key. It is very interesting to recall that the ancient Chinese regarded the garden as a refuge from 'the noisiness of the world, from the confining walls of habitation'. In other words, an extension of the home where one can relax and find relief from tension; this surely is as important in present-day landscaping as it was in the days of ancient China.

With a waterside garden, it is necessary to protect the bank from the ravages of wash and floods by using one of the methods already described (see pp. 31-45). However, it is very important to keep the freeboard (height from normal water level to top of campshedding) as low as practicable. If a large boat is to be moored, then a higher campshedding may be needed for the length of that craft: if carried out for the entire length of the property, the frontage may look more like a wharf than a garden.

If there is a steep and fairly high bank that requires protection, do not campshed this to the top, keep it a reasonable level and, subject to water authority approval, bring it out some three feet from the bank, or cut the bank away by this amount to provide, after backfilling, a convenient landing and mooring area. Inboard of this area the vertical bank can then be protected from the ravages of floods by building a brick or stone wall which can be relieved by an interesting flight of steps. There is a great variety of bricks from which to choose, both in colour and texture, but do not use faced bricks which may flake when hard frosts follow a flood. This too applies to the choice of stone; Cotswold and similar walling can absorb a vast quantity of water in times of high flood and will rapidly disintegrate if frosts ensue.

If a high riverbank is steep but not vertical, then retain the campshedding or revetment as suggested above, but grade the land behind to an easy angle which will allow flood water to flow smoothly and with little or no damage. After all there is nothing that looks better than a fine sweep of lawn down to the waterside.

Back to the landing area: this is best surfaced if it is being used for moorings, fishing or just sitting out. So many properties are made dull and unimaginative with a long strip of concrete along the river front, which at its best is often badly laid and with complete disregard for expansion joints. Paving with rectangular slabs is practical and attractive. The use of real stone is ideal but it must be mentioned that a hard-wearing one, such as York stone, can become dangerously slippery by the waterside. There are many manufactured paving units from which to choose, whilst the old Victorian type clay paviors are back on the market as well as an excellent range of paving bricks. At a glance the modern coloured concrete block paving, now being used by so many local authorities, gives the impression of brick. Choice abounds of ways to contrast hard landscaping with domestic building materials.

The old school of landscapers laid their paving slabs and herringbone or other styles of brick paths on soil (usually screened, or sieved, to be free from stones). Like many things, we are turning full circle: 'flexible paving' is now popular with much of it being laid in shopping precincts and pedestrian areas. This technique consists of laying traditional clay brick, or in some instances concrete blocks, without mortar: they are laid on a bed of sand and firmed in with a vibrator. Today, there is a wonderful selection of bricks from which to choose so giving warmth and charm to any garden.

Another old medium that is returning is granite setts. They make a superb surface for a river frontage and with skill, can be laid to form most delightful patterns. I know of one old Thames mill where the landing area and other surfaces are paved with setts which unite buildings and gardens most attractively.

Alternatives are the use of timber decking which can look rural

Campshedding on a river bank where the ground rises sharply, incorporating a higher section for mooring, a paved landing area with a retaining stone wall. The remainder of bank graded to an easy angle.

Landing stage constructed with machine-turned and prepared timbers, pressure-treated with preservative for a forty-year life.

and rugged whilst enjoying a long life if properly treated; or stone chippings, pea gravel or similar. The range of chippings is wide, having been crushed from stone quarried over widely differing areas so giving a considerable choice of colours. If laying stone chippings or gravel then it is wise, after consolidating and levelling the ground, to lay filter cloth (membrane) before covering with the chippings. Water will drain through the membrane but mud will not ooze up and furthermore stone will not tread into the ground and be lost.

However the waterside is finished, it is a good idea to make some planting bays for native waterside plants such as the delightful yellow flag, water forget-me-nots, flowering rush, purple loosestrife and so on. At this juncture I deem it wise to proffer a little advice to the aspiring do-it-yourself enthusiast; if you have ageing and subsiding timber campshedding with or without a landing stage, do not emulate those riparian owners who have fallen into the age-old trap of making good and levelling up the frontage with bulk concrete. Mass concrete is extremely heavy, so adding considerable top weight simply hastens the collapse of the old structure. As it collapses concrete falls on to the bed of the river, which at a later date has to be cleared, often with difficulty and at considerable expense, before a new campshedding can be driven. If it is desirable to tidy up an old frontage on a short-term basis, then construct a frame of galvanized steel tubing with the easy fix couplings of the Kee-Klamp type and then clad the frame with timber to suit the situation.

When major river works have to be carried out in a rural area, such as diverting a watercourse for the building of a motorway, a flood relief scheme or some other reason, then landscaping is essentially a case of skilfully blending the new with the old whilst ensuring that the most suitable species and varieties of trees are planted.

Due attention must be paid to the wildflower population. In some cases it makes good sense to lift existing plants with a really good ball of soil, or sod of turf, and keep them going in nursery beds until they can be re-planted on the new site. We have however been greatly helped in recent years by the seed trade of this country; both national seedsmen and individual specialist firms alike have made a great contribution to conservation by producing a truly remarkable range of wildflower seed for use in general landscaping as well as creating habitats for the encouragement of seed-eating birds, butterflies and bees. With the availability of waterside wildflower seed, it is now possible to make good an eroded riverbank down to the last detail; the wildflower seed can be incorporated with a suitable grass seed mixture, thus simplifying the sowing procedure. Sowing wildflower seed is like charity: it begins at home. Even the smallest area available can receive its quota of seed, so helping to build up our waterside flora, be it purple loosestrife, water forget-me-not, marsh marigold, water avens, meadow-sweet, hemp agrimony, water mint or devil's bit scabious. Two gorgeous specimens are the snake's head fritillary and the loddon lily, both of which can be grown from bulbs available from specialist producers. I remember some years back a meadow alongside a small, but well known river, where fritillaries flowered in profusion. The farmer who owned this land appreciated not only their beauty but was aware of their scarcity, so he only mowed part of the meadow every year which gave the fritillaries the opportunity not only of seeding but also germinating. There are still some 'secret' meadows such as this and one in particular seems to have become known without any damage to the flora. As a very rough guide the sowing rate for wild flowers is 15 Kg per acre (1 Kg will cover approximately 270 square metres, or 50 gm. will cover around 16 sq. yd). Due attention must be paid to re-establishing emergent water plants too, and, better still, creating new plantations. In the trade it is often possible to obtain plants without much difficulty; for the private owner requiring a fairly wide selection in limited numbers, it is sensible to mention that there are a goodly number of aquatic plant nurseries which give an excellent service with prompt delivery.

With many landscaping schemes, be they private or funded by a public authority, the old howler is not infrequently made – that all the work is carried out to a beautiful site plan, but without viewing the expanse of the project from the water. Unless local authority officers are boating men they completely overlook the wisdom of hiring a boat so as to get a proper perspective of their riparian domains.

9

Boats

No book on waterways would be complete without a few words on boats and boating. Being the sort of person who enjoys using a pair of sculls, the open air and camping, my choice is a Thames dinghy, skiff or gig. Of course, craft such as these, together with punts and canoes, are environmentally pleasing due to the fact that they are silent and make no wash. Until a few years ago, they tended to be scarce and were possibly considered old fashioned. However, with the formation of the Thames Traditional Boat Society back in 1979, the interest in these craft has gone from strength to strength with old craft being resurrected and restored and new craft to original designs being built from high-quality timber and materials to old-fashioned standards.

With the success of this society it was not long before motor boat enthusiasts set up the Thames Vintage Boat Club for those who were the proud owners of delightful and aged vessels that were specifically designed and built for use on inland and confined waters. Such is the interest that old craft which could be loosely termed 'wrecks' are being restored to their former pristine glory by enthusiastic and hardworking owners. The interest is now gearing up to the extent that there are a number of skilled boat builders engaged in constructing replicas of these fine craft. This in itself is a contribution towards conservation of our waterways, inasmuch that as the majority of these old boats (and their replicas) were, and are, designed for ease of manoeuvrability with minimum of wash; this, with the fact that their owners pride themselves on good handling, sets an excellent example in watermanship.

Originating from the canals, we have our pleasure narrow boats of various lengths, the design of which is based on the old traditional working boats. They have much to commend them and they make little wash or disturbance.

Another interesting organization of recent years is the Electric Boat Association, formed to cope with great re-vitalization of electric power, which provides quiet, vibrationless and fume-free boating. The movement is progressing so well that British Waterways Board is planning to produce a leaflet giving full details of 30 amp charging points around the entire waterway system. Several firms are now making beautiful clean running hulls for electric propulsion whilst the entirely new Lynch electric motor is proving itself a great step forward. It is the brainchild of British inventor Cedric Lynch. Firms on the Norfolk Broads, Thames and the canals are now using electric powered launches for day and/or hourly hire besides passenger trips. When the Broads Authority set up a new wildlife water trail to run through the nature reserve near Ludham, they opted to obtain an electric launch for the purpose.

Old-fashioned steam boats and their replicas have their devotees and there are some wonderful examples of these very quiet and charming craft around our waterways. Their hull design generally bears a strong resemblance to their electric counterparts and it is for this reason that they are usually very clean running, making but little wash. The Steam Boat Association of Great Britain is a well established society looking after the interests of steam boat enthusiasts across the country, and, by the way, those interested in viewing steam boats in their own environment should not fail to visit the Steam Boat Museum on Lake Windermere.

On the Thames and other rivers many modern boats are of multi-purpose design and make far too much wash. Often this is due to the craft having shallow draught, high windage factor, powerful engines and small fast revving propellers, hence speed has to be maintained in order to control steerage way. Some modern boat salesmen, in common with motor dealers, tend to sell craft on the merits of their glamorous specifications which is not always helpful to the novice, who in the old days would go to his local boatman who would logically evaluate his customer's requirements and recommend a boat for his specific purpose.

The Inland Waterways Amenity Advisory Council has carried out much research on the design of recreational craft but I fear it will take a long time for their results to filter through and have everyday impact upon our waterways.

As this century draws on, boating upon our rivers and canals is becoming more popular than ever: we must come to terms with this fact if we are to maintain our waterside environment. Excessive wash is one of the problems that must be overcome if we are to maintain our lush waterside flora; often the smaller species disappear completely; even water lilies and yellow brandy bottles require calm conditions, hence their scarcity. In time the worst affected sections of bank have to be repaired, then, according to the method used, wildlife is more often than not offered no hospitality. This 'little by little' process adds up to a mighty lot over the years, as I have witnessed since my boyhood afloat some sixty years ago.

Glossary

ait, eyot
an island. There are earlier variations in spelling.

bog
mire in which acid-loving plants grow.

campshedding
the protection and retention of a riverbank or watercourse with a sheathing of timber, or in modern times interlocking steel sheets. 'To campshed' is a variation of the eighteenth-century term to campshot; since the 1970s the variation 'to campsheet' has been creeping in. The *Oxford English Dictionary* describes 'campshott' as 'A facing of piles and boarding along the bank of a river, or the side of an embankment to protect the bank from the action of the current, or to resist the out-thrust of the embankment.' The name 'campshot' goes back to the days when Dutch water engineers were plying their skills in this country, including the 'side boarding of watercourses', which in their native tongue was 'Kant schot'. This name was seemingly unkind to the English tongue and soon became 'campshot'. This type of work is referred to as 'quayheading' on the Norfolk Broads. In some instances the term 'bulkheading' is used, as in America.

cantilevered piles
see piling

coffer dam
a temporary watertight enclosure, usually made by driving piles, after which the water can be pumped out, e.g. when building a weir or structures rising from the bed of a waterway.

drawdock
a creek or inlet into which barges can be run to load or unload. Sometimes referred to as a parish wharf, generally when man-made at right-angles to the navigation.

duckbills
a special type of anchor for waling (patented in England and America) for use where ground and/or bank conditions are difficult.

87

faggoting
an old fashioned form of bank protection, which consisted of making up and tying brushwood into handy bundles, known as 'faggots' or 'kids'. The faggots were placed in the desired position along the water's edge and pegged down. Positioning the faggots was a matter of experience and skill so that they trapped sediment and silt as the water flow was slowed down by protruding twigs and branches.

fen
mire in which neutral or alkaline-loving plants grow.

flash
rush of water downriver.

gabions
an official description states that they are 'a wicker basket of cylindrical form, usually open at both ends, intended to be filled with earth for use in fortifications and engineering'. This description reads as though it might be a literal translation from a Roman army instruction manual. Admittedly, gabions in Roman times were made of wicker but in an assortment of shapes and sizes as they are today, except that the modern counterparts are made from woven galvanized wire and often plastic coated for further protection, whilst the filling is of stone, crushed concrete or gravel rejects.

geotextiles
this term covers a galaxy of mainly modern materials that are woven, or in some instances extruded, from a wide range of substances most of which are synthetic: one particular type of mesh that holds loose ground together until nature has taken over is fabricated from a bio-degradable material. An excellent material for long-term use is now freely available, which consists of high-tenacity nylon threads which are welded where they cross, so giving thousands of empty spaces per square metre, thus making it ideal for filling with gravel, soil, or material as preferred. These are but two examples of the way geotextiles protect the top layer of soil against erosion whilst encouraging plant growth.

gull, gutt
part of a river where water is shallow and fast flowing.

ham, hamm
a peninsula formed by the meander of a river; sometimes the river breaks through the neck of a ham to transform it into an island.

hole
short section or area of a river where the water is exceptionally deep; caused by the action of eddies and/or underwater currents acting on soft stratum in the river bed.

hythe, hard
a public landing place for passengers or merchandise.

kid
is associated with 'kiddle', a form of weir made with brushwood for the trapping of fish and which was sometimes referred to as a 'fishery hedge'. It possibly goes without saying that osiers form very good material using varieties such as *Salix purpurea*, *Salix viminalis*, etc; thicker osiers, i.e. 2 - 3 in. diameter not only make excellent stakes for pegging down but root easily, so making a strong attractive bank. 'Spiling' is a variation on the above method; willow stakes are still driven into the river bed, but instead of placing faggots withies (willow) are woven around the stakes. The willow stakes, once rooted, provide living long term bank protection.

landwater
a quick run-off into a watercourse after heavy rain or quick thaw; resultant sudden increases in flow known as 'freshes'.

left-hand bank
the left-hand bank when travelling downstream; rivers are always 'handed' from source downstream, so on proceeding upstream the left-hand bank will be on the right-hand side. Likewise all structures such as locks, weirs and bridges are numbered from source downwards.

meander
the way in which a river winds about in its course. Derived from the Latin *'maeander'*. The Romans named a river thus in Phrygia (Turkey). There is also a River Meander in Alberta.

membranes
another modern innovation; they are made from continuous filaments of polypropylene. Generally they are supplied in large rolls which can be cut with ease to suit the situation; this material is often referred to as stabilization matting or filter cloth due to its ability to allow the passage of water whilst retaining the minutest particles of solid matter.

mire
area of peat that is permanently wet.

ox-bow
a crescent-shaped pool, formed when meanders on an uncontrolled river become exaggerated, so that in the process of time the loops meet. Once united, the river flows through in a direct route, so abandoning the old crescent-shaped course which eventually becomes cut off due to the deposition of silt.

piling
there are two types, one being free standing piles of squared timber or box steel sections driven into the river bed for the mooring of houseboats and large craft whilst cantilevered piles are made of heavy section steel, of considerable depth and width with interlocking clutches. They are a kind of piling. They are driven to a good depth and because of their substantial design can under certain soil conditions be used without waling *(q.v.)* or tie rods *(q.v.)*, hence the word 'cantilever'. Piling is normally relegated to the construction of wharves and docks, or where a river bank has to take heavy loading such as a factory.

Portadam
a registered patent. With this there is no need to drive or withdraw piles, suitable for lighter structures.

revetment
defined in dictionary as 'a facing of masonry, concrete, sods, etc, supporting a bank or embankment'. To this general description can be added bricks, hessian (or polypropylene) bags filled with concrete, gabions and certain proprietary cast-concrete sections in various configurations.

right-hand bank
see left-hand bank.

riparian owner
anyone owning property alongside a natural watercourse. Under common law any such owner possesses responsibilities and rights belonging to the stretch of watercourse which falls within the boundaries of his property. Normally it is presumed that a riparian owner owns land up to the centre line of a non-tidal watercourse.

sheet piling
campshedding on canals with lightweight interlocking steel sheets (a British Waterways Board term).

shoal
a shallow area.

tie rods and anchors
self evident names for the method of anchoring the top of a camp-shedding back to the bank.

waling, whaling
the horizontal member giving lateral support to the top of a camp-shedding.

water table
the level under the ground in permeable or porous rock below which the ground is completely saturated with water. Sometimes referred to as 'water level'.

Bibliography

Books

Adams,Thompson & Fry, *Survey of the Thames for Middlesex and Surrey County Councils* (St Dominics Press, 1930)

Chaplin,Mary, *Riverside Gardening* (W.H. & L. Collingridge Ltd, 1964)

Chaplin,Peter H., *The Thames from source to tideway* (Whittet Books, 1982, 1988)

Chaplin,Tom, *The Narrow Boat Book* (Whittet Books, 1978) *Narrow Boats* (Whittet Books, 1989)

Council for the Preservation of Rural England, *Thames Valley Cricklade to Staines* (1929)

Rivers of Great Britain, 2 volumes (Cassell, 1889)

A.S. Wisdom, *The Law of Rivers and Watercourses* (Shaw, 1979)

Periodicals and handbooks

Architectural Review, 'The Linear National Park', by Eric de Maré (July 1950)

Conservation and land drainage guidelines, Waterspace Amenity Council, 1980

'Enkamat as a construction material in civil engineering', Enka, Arnhem, Holland

'Flexible linings for canals and watercourses', R.Agostini and A.Papetti, Maccaferri, Bologna, Italy

'Nature Conservation and river engineering', Nature Conservancy Council, 1983

Waterway Architecture – an economic return from conservation (Inland Waterways Amenity Advisory Council, 1985)

Waterway Environment Handbook, Peter White (British Waterways Board. 1st edition, 1972)

Maps

A map of England showing rivers and navigable canals and those which have been proposed. By T.Conder 1792

Nicholson's. The Ordnance Survey Inland Waterways Map of Great Britain, 1987

Inland Navigation Authorities

British Waterways Board publish a complete list together with addresses and telephone numbers in their Waterway User's Companion.

Useful Addresses

Wildflower Seeds
John Chambers, 15 Westleigh Road,
Barton Seagrave, Kettering, Northants NN15 5AJ

T.Harrison Chaplin Ltd., Meadhurst Park Nursery,
Cadbury Road, Sunbury-on-Thames, Middx TW16 7LZ

Emorsgate Seeds, Terrington Court, Terrington St. Clement,
Kings Lynn, Norfolk PE34 4NT

Suffolk Herbs, Sawyers Farm, Little Cornard,
Sudbury, Suffolk CO10 0NY

There are also wholesale seed merchants dealing with wild flowers
such as British Seed Houses, Johnsons Seeds and others.

Popular brands of seed sold in shops, market a limited range of
wildflowers, such as Suttons and Mr Fothergill.

Wildfowl
Waveney Wildfowl, Brook Farm, Kirby Cane, Bungay, Suffolk NR35 2PJ
sell an interesting range of ornamental waterfowl.

Aquatic and waterside plants
Anglo Aquarium Plant Co. Ltd, Strayfield Road, Enfield, Middlesex
EN2 9JE

Anthony Archer-Wills, Gaypools Nurseries, Gay Street, Nr Pulbor-
ough, West Sussex RH20 2HH

British willow furniture, baskets, domestic and garden requirements, etc
Ex stock or custom made:
The English Basket Centre, Curload, Stoke St Gregory, Taunton,
Somerset TA3 6JD

Gadsby & Son, Burrowbridge, Bridgwater, Somerset TA7 0JL

P.H. Coate & Son, Meare Green Court, Stoke St Gregory, Taunton,
Somerset

Willow and poplar trees
Edgar Watts Ltd, Willow Works, Sawmills and Nurseries, Bungay,
Suffolk NR35 1BW who are the largest growers and producers of
English willow clefts for cricket bats in the world.

Index

gardens, riverside, 80-81
geotextiles, 44-8, 64
Gould (John) Ltd 20
Grand Union Canal 19, 64
Grand Union Canal Company 34
gravel (bank surfaces) 83
great crested grebes 61, **61**
Great Ouse Restoration Society 20
greenheart (timber) 44
Greywell Tunnel 63
Guildford barges 16

HEMLOCK FIR SPRUCE **77**, 78
herons 60-61, **61**
honey fungus 80
Humber keels 15
Humber, R. 15
Hutchings, David 19

INLAND WATERWAYS AMENITY ADVISORY
COUNCIL 86
Inland Waterways Association 20
Iris pseudacorus 27
Irwell, R. 15
islands 53-6

JETTIES 72

KENNET AND AVON CANAL TRUST 20
Kennet, R. 16, 23, 63

LAMPREYS 63
landing stages 72, **83**
law, waterway navigation 16
·Leeds and Liverpool Canal 43
little grebes 61, **61**
Llangollen Canal 67
loddon lily 84
London River Yacht Club 48
Lower Avon Navigation Trust 19
Lynch, Cedric 86
Lynch electric motors 85-6

MACCAFERRI GABIONS **42**, 53
marinas 71, 72
Marriage, John 20-21
marsh warblers 62-3
Mersey, R. 15
Metasequoia glyptostroboides **77**, 78
Minsmere 21
Missouri, R. 48
Monoslabs, 40, **41**
moorings 72, **82**
Munk, Lionel 21

NARROW BOATS 16, 85

National Parks Commission 55
National Rivers Authority 17, 18
National Trust 21, 23
Nene, R. **18**
Newbury barges 16
Nicolon 46-8, **47**
Nicospan 46, 64
Nile pike 52
nitrate pollution 50-51
Norfolk
Broads 15, 18, 28, 51, 55, 86
keels 15, 28
wherries 15, 28
Nuphar lutea 55
Nymphaea alba 55

Ocotea rubra 44
osiers 74
otter holts, artificial 65, **65**
otters 62, 65
Ouse (Great), R. 20
Ouse (Yorkshire), R. 21
Oxford Canal **35**, 43, 67, **67**, **68**

PALMER, GRAHAM 16-20
paving 82
peatlands 21-2, 23, 28
Phalaris arundinacea 27
Phragmites lacustris 26-7
piling 31-2, 34-6, **35**, 38, 44
planting, waterside 28, 74-81, 84
pollarding 75, **75**
pollution, water 49-52
poplar 77-8
Populus
  balsamifera 77
  canescens 77
  nigra 77
  tremula 78
Porcupine blocks 40, **40**
Port Meadow, Oxford 63

REED CANARY GRASS 27
reed, common 26-7
reed mace 26
Residential Boat Owners' Association 51
restoration (groups, etc.) 18-23
  see also under name
revetments 29, 36-8, **39**, 42-8, 81
Rhus typhina 78
river management 57-8
River Stour Trust 20-21
River Wey Navigation 23
Rochdale Canal 21
Roman Britain 14
ronds 28